ESSEX
ON THE
MAP

The 18th century
Land Surveyors
of Essex

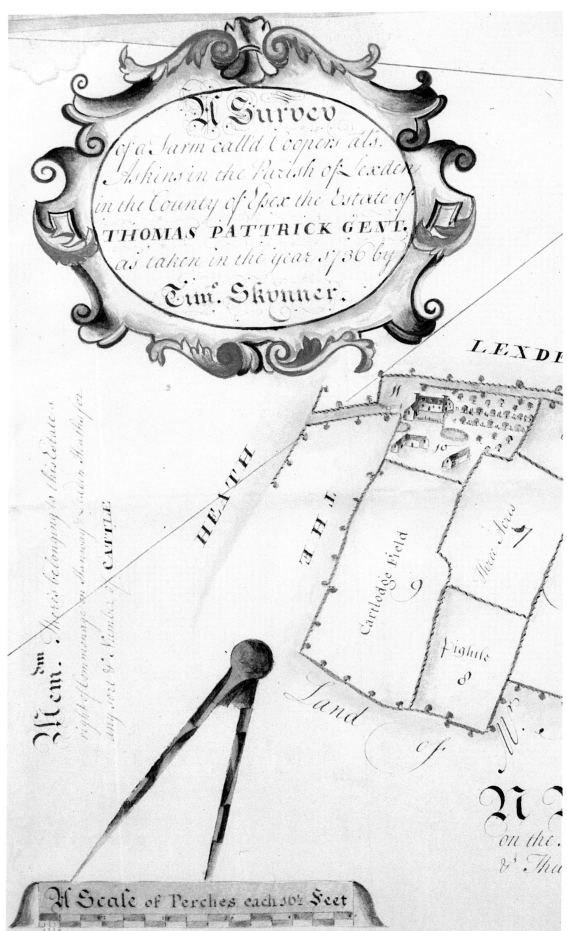

A Survey of a Farm call'd Coopers als. Askins in the Parish of Lexden in the County of Essex the Estate of THOMAS PATTRICK GENT. as taken in the year 1736 by Tim. Skynner.

LEXDE

HEATH

THE

Cartlodge Field 9

Three Acre 7

Fighils 8

Land of

A Scale of Perches each 16½ Feet

ESSEX
ON THE
MAP

The 18th century
Land Surveyors
of Essex

by A. Stuart Mason MA, MD, FRCP

Foreword by Dr Helen Wallis

Published by ESSEX RECORD OFFICE
1990

Published by the

ESSEX RECORD OFFICE

County Hall, Chelmsford, Essex CM1 1LX

© *ESSEX COUNTY COUNCIL 1990*

BRITISH LIBRARY CATALOGUING IN PUBLICATION DATA
Mason, A. Stuart
    Essex on the map: the 18th century land surveyors of Essex
    1. Essex. Cartography. Biographies. Collections
    I. Title II. Essex Record Office
    526.0922
    ISBN 0-900360-75-5

Essex Record Office Publication No 105

Set in 10/13pt Baskerville
Designed by Keith Mirams MCSD
Printed in England by Lavenham Press

Contents

List of Illustrations

Foreword

*E*NGLISH ESTATE SURVEYS were a special kind of map, made as aids for the management of land. Although utilitarian, many plans were finely decorated and intended for display, reflecting the landowner's pride of possession. The thousands of plans which survive from a period of some 350 years of surveying activity document in graphic detail the evolution of the rural landscape.

The beginnings of estate mapping date from the reign of Elizabeth I, 1558 to 1603. Before that land surveys had been primarily recorded by written description. By the time of Elizabeth's death, geometrical methods of survey had become a regular practice, although levels of skill were variable. Men turned to this new form of employment without relevant practical experience. The Essex surveyor Ralph Agas told how on coming to London he encountered "a plaine Table man (marry he was a plumber and had learned from a Painter)".[1] A check on the man's surveys showed them to be inaccurate. The surveyor Edward Worsop complained of the shortcomings of practitioners in similar terms: "Everie man knoweth that lande is our riches in the hyest nature, and yet true surveying, and valuing thereof is shoufled up, as though it were a matter of small importance."[2]

Worsop went on to propose a "Faculty of Surveyors" (as Edward Lynam describes it), whose members had certified qualifications:[3] "If the skilful in the parts Mathematicall, Legal and Judicial would frindly and singly joyne together to reforme, and instruct each other, and to reduce surveie to a perfect order: without doubt many which understand but parts . . . would in short space prove sufficient men."[4]

Worsop touched on another problem: "The common people for the most part are in great feare when surveie is made of their land." The surveyor had to deal with the natural suspicions of farmers and tenants against this "upstart art". John Norden set out the complaints and the answers to them in *The Surveyors Dialogue* (London, 1607). The surveyor argued that "Surveys are necessarie and profitable both for Lord and Tennant." The farmer asserted: "oftentimes you are the cause that men lose their land." The surveyor responded that "the faulty are afraid to be seene . . . the innocent need not feare to be looked into".[5] These words must have seemed cold comfort to the anxious farmer or tenant.

The farmer questioned the motives and need for surveying, and remarked, "is not the field it selfe a goodly Map for the Lord to looke upon, better then a painted paper: And what is he the better to see it laid out in colours: He can adde nothing to his land, nor diminish ours: and therefore that labour above all may be saved." The surveyor pointed to the advantage to the landlord: "The Lord sitting in his chayre, may see what he hath, where and how it lyeth, and in whose use and occupation every particular is upon the suddaine view."[6]

By the time the fourth edition of Norden's *Surveyors Dialogue* was printed in 1738, estate surveying was accepted as a normal procedure. The textbooks on estate management published in the eighteenth century stated that one of the primary duties of a steward to his lord was to ensure proper surveys be undertaken.

The golden age of the local land surveyor was the period 1700 to 1850. A prosperous landed gentry was eager to have estates managed by modern methods. The surveyors themselves were benefiting from the advances in mathematical instruction which followed the Restoration in 1660. "The Mathematicks" had become one of the most popular studies. John Aubrey the antiquary commented in 1690, "it was Edmund Gunter who, with his Booke of the

Quadrant, Sector and Cross-Staffe did open men's understandings and made young men in love with that Studie. Before, the Mathematicall Sciences were lock't up in the Greeke and Latin tongues and there lay untoucht, kept safe in some libraries. After Mr. Gunter published his Booke, these Sciences sprang up amain, more and more to that height it is now."[7] Gunter had been a mathematical teacher and then Professor of Astronomy at Gresham College. His inventions included "Gunter's chain", henceforward a basic instrument for land survey.

In the later years of the seventeenth century instruction in mathematics and the use of maps and charts became available in the shops of London dealers. Thomas Tuttell at his two shops offered instruction in "all parts of the Mathematics" (including the use of instruments). One Master advertised "Geography made Easy, and the Use of all the ordinary Sorts of Charts and Maps, whither Geographical, Hydrographical, Plans, Groundplots, or Perspectives, Taught in a Week's time . . .". Referring to "this Necessary, Pleasant and Easy Science", he continued, "It is taught to either Sex, whether Learned in other Sciences or not, if they be above the Age of twelve years . . ."[8]

Dr John Wallis, the celebrated Oxford mathematician, was to recall "Mathematicks at that time, with us, were scarce looked upon as Academical Studies, but rather Mechanical; as the business of Traders, Merchants, Seamen, Carpenters, Surveyors of Lands, or the like, and perhaps some Almanack Makers in London . . . For the Study of Mathematicks was at that time more cultivated in London than in the Universities."[9]

The opportunities for instruction in mathematics brought a wide variety of men into surveying. Although some of their surveys have been lost many survive, often in lawyers' offices. F. G. Emmison estimated in 1966 that more than 20,000 pre-1850 private estate maps were in public repositories.[10] Most of the maps are now in the county record offices of England and Wales. Published catalogues and indexes provide valuable guides for their use.

The need for a national dictionary of surveyors was also recognized. The late Edward Lynam, Superintendent of the Map Room of the British Museum, proposed such a dictionary to the county archivist F. W. Steer in 1947. Steer took up the project and between 1958 and 1964 had compiled from the returns of questionnaires an index of almost 3000 surveyors from the records of some 30,000 to 40,000 maps. In 1966 Steer presented the material to the Department of English Local History at the University of Leicester, where Peter Eden carried on the work. His *Dictionary of Land Surveyors* in four parts was published in 1975. Eden recently passed his records to Sarah Bendall of Emanuel College, Cambridge. She is putting the dictionary on computer, which will increase its usefulness.

Dr Stuart Mason has now added to the literature this detailed study of the surveyors who worked in Essex. He chose Essex because of the large number of maps in the Record Office at Chelmsford. Under a series of distinguished archivists, F. G. Emmison, the late Kenneth Newton and currently Victor Gray, the Essex Record Office has been a pioneer in the acquisition, preservation and recording of estate plans. The excellent *Catalogue of Maps in the Essex Record Office* (Chelmsford 1947), by F. G. Emmison with its three printed supplements is a model of its kind. More recently A. C. Edwards and K. C. Newton in their book, *The Walkers of Hanningfield* (Dover, 1984) have documented the outstanding achievements of these Essex surveyors of the late Tudor period.

Stuart Mason concentrates on the eighteenth century, the heyday of estate surveying. He has checked a wide range of sources including advertisements in local newspapers to build up a picture of the lives and backgrounds of those concerned with surveying.

His researches reveal many aspects of rural life. A list of alternative occupations which surveyors pursued (p. 6) shows a diversity of activities, from auctioneers and brewers to instrument makers and military engineers, with school masters in the majority. As the century advanced, and the lease and sale of property became more important, surveyors and lawyers developed a close relationship. Valuers and attorneys became more prominent. A hierarchy of functionaries is evident (pp. 18–22). Gentlemen surveyors concerned with the valuation of estates were doing work more comparable with the modern chartered surveyor. The land measurer was ranked as an artisan.

It is interesting to note only a slight connection between surveying and cartographic publishing (p. 25). The Huguenots John Rocque and his brother-in-law Bernard Scalé, together with their friend Peter André, are among the exceptions. The difference in overheads between the two occupations may explain this. The land surveyor's overheads were relatively low. Stuart Mason reports that in the 1740s a plain table and level would cost £8-8-0; Humphrey Repton in 1788 bought a theodolite and level for £10 and a chain for £0-8-6. According to Richeson a fully equipped surveyor in 1800 might lay out £125,[11] but surveying with chain was still the basic technique. While Elizabethan mapmakers mention instruments in their wills, eighteenth-century surveyors do not appear to do so.

Map publishers, on the other hand, had to meet the cost of premises, copperplate engraving, printing, sale and distribution. The bankruptcy (in 1766) of one of the leading publishers of the eighteenth century, Thomas Jefferys, geographer to the king, is ascribed to the expenses incurred in undertaking his county surveys.[12]

Although Stuart Mason ends his study in 1800, he reveals trends indicating the future fortunes of the estate surveyor. The founding of the Surveyors' Club took place in 1792, but the members were surveyors of buildings, mainly architects. The Land Surveyors' Club followed in 1834, and the Royal Institute of Chartered Surveyors in 1851. Thus Worsop's desire for a professional body was at last fulfilled. At the same time, the Ordnance Survey's printed large scale plans greatly reduced the work of the private surveyor. Significantly, Norden's *Surveyors Dialogue* was published again in 1851, but by the Architectural Association, in appreciation of the book's contemporary relevance: "it appears a work peculiarly fitted to the temper of the present times when the Architect, far more frequently than any other professional authority, is called upon to offer that advice, as to the best disposition of landed property, which he is as often entrusted to carry into effect." The role of the land measurer had been taken over by experts in valuation and architecture.

In 1954 E. G. R. Taylor described her book on the mathematical practitioners of Tudor and Stuart England as "a chronicle of lesser men – teachers, textbook writers, technicians, craftsmen – but for whom great scientists would always remain sterile in their generation".[13] The Essex estate surveyors in a similar way were mainly "lesser men", some merely known as a name on a plan. Only a few enjoyed a national reputation. Yet in one way or another they contributed to the proper management of land and were key figures in the rural community.

In documenting the activities of such men, Stuart Mason has added a major work to cartographic literature. Its significance extends beyond the county of Essex. It throws light on the history of estate surveying throughout the countryside of England.

Helen Wallis

Notes

1 Ralph Agas, *Preparative to platting of landes and tenements for surveigh* (London, 1596), p.

2 Edward Worsop, *A Discoverie of sundrie errours and faults daily committed by Landemeaters*, London 1582.

3 Edward Lynam, *The Mapmaker's Art* (London, 1953), pp. 62–3.

4 Worsop, sig. K.2.

5 John Norden, *The Surveyors Dialogue* (London, 1607), marginal notes to pp. 3,

6 Norden, 1607, pp. 15–16.

7 O. L. Dick (ed.), *Aubrey's Brief Lives* (London, 1950), p. xxxii.

8 British Library, Bagford Collection, Harl. 5947, no. 101.

9 Quoted in E. G. R. Taylor, *Mathematical Practitioners of Tudor and Stuart England* (Cambridge, 1954), p. 4.

10 F. G. Emmison, *Archives and Local History* (London, 1966), p.62.

11 Richeson, *English Land Measuring* (MIT Press, 1966).

12 J. B. Harley, "The bankruptcy of Thomas Jefferys", *Imago Mundi*, vol. XX (1966), pp 27–48.

13 E. G. R. Taylor, p. xi.

Acknowledgements

THIS BOOK MARKS my enjoyment of old manuscript maps and my admiration for their makers. It is a pleasure to thank the many people in many places whose ready help has made my task a happy one. In particular I am most grateful to all the staff of the Essex Record Office at Chelmsford who gave me at all times their skilled assistance with such goodwill that I always look forward to my next visit.

I want to thank Dr F. G. Emmison, whose work in forming a unique collection of maps at the Record Office first stimulated my interest in Essex cartography and then provided the means for this study.

I owe the publication of this book to the cheerful energy of Victor Gray, County Archivist and lover of maps. I thank him for his constant encouragement and for guiding the book through the labyrinth of production, the cost of which was generously supported by the Friends of Historic Essex. The work of the Friends in helping publications should be publicly acknowledged and applauded, as it is by this grateful author.

I was privileged to have had my manuscript read by Dr Helen Wallis, until recently Map Librarian, the British Library. I have adopted her suggestions and the remaining errors are entirely my own. I thank her for the hard work she has done and for agreeing to write a foreword to the book.

I am well aware that this study cannot be definitive. There must still be estate maps that have not come to the attention of the Essex Record Office and personal details of the cartographers known only to their descendants. So I appeal to any one who has an Essex estate map or knowledge of the cartographer to contact the County Archivist. In this way our knowledge of a worthy body of men, whose work was essential to 18th century Essex, may be extended.

Stuart Mason
Gidea Park 1990

The photographs for the illustrations were taken by Mick Hammond, photographer to the Essex Record Office

PART ONE

Maps and Surveying

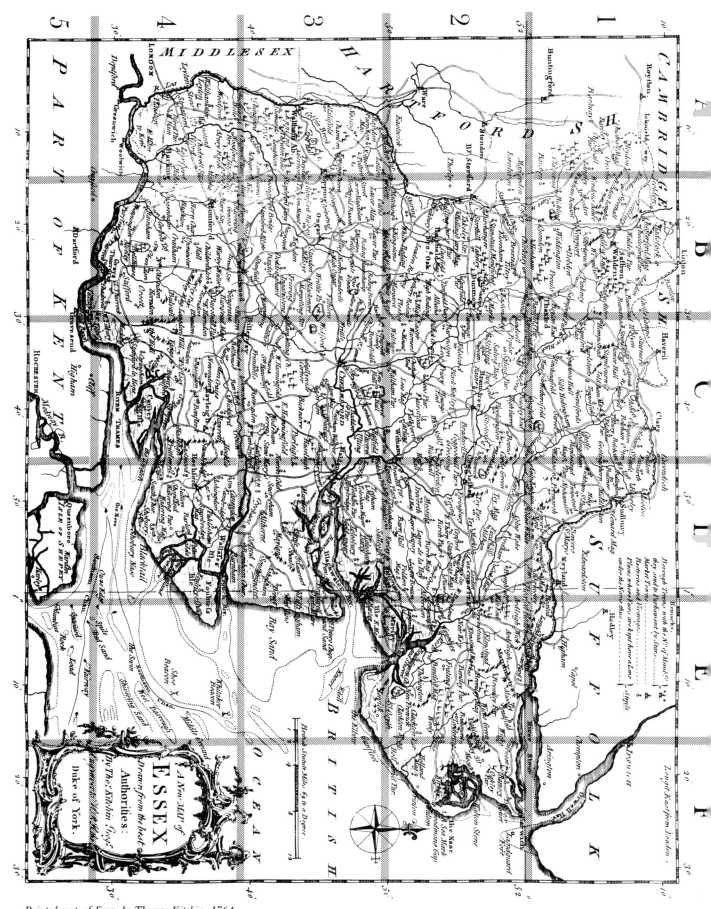

Printed map of Essex by Thomas Kitchin, 1764.
The overlaid grid should be used in conjunction with the Index to locate Essex place-names referred to in the text.

Introduction

"In their fashioning, as in their content, English estate and manorial plans differ from all other kinds of maps. They were drawn and decorated by country surveyors for the information and pleasure of country squires."[1] These maps are also a good source of information about their makers, so Edward Lynam's words are a fitting motto for this study of land surveyors working in Essex during the 18th century.

The choice of a whole county as an area for study has the advantage of allowing a comparison of surveyors who lived within the county and those who were brought in from neighbouring counties, the Metropolis or from afar. Business and family connections between local surveyors can be explored and an attempt can be made to find out what sort of client chose what sort of surveyor. The personal choice of Essex as the county for study was only possible because of the large number of estate maps held by the Essex Record Office.

Confining the study to the 18th century is an arbitrary but convenient choice of a slice of time from the continuum of history. The few pioneering land surveyors had long since made their mark and their contributions have been well researched. There is no better example of Elizabethan and Jacobean land measurers than the Walkers of Hanningfield, whose work was so ably described by Edwards and Newton.[2] The organisation of land surveyors into a profession had to await the founding in 1834 of the Land Surveyors' Club, the forerunner of the Institute of Chartered Surveyors.[3]

In 18th century Essex land surveyors were numerous, often part-time and from varied backgrounds. They were engaged in measuring land that had been measured before and in redefining boundaries and land usage. The century saw in Essex the continued decline of the cloth industry and the expansion of agriculture.[4] Fortunes made in the City or abroad were invested in land. The declining economy of the towns was matched by rising land values. Enclosure was not a feature for, as Arthur Young[5] wrote at the end of the century, "Essex has for three years been an enclosed county – no field here for the great parliamentary exertions which have been made in some many counties". There were less than half a dozen enclosure awards for Essex before the end of the century, compared with counties like Bedfordshire where the proportion of enclosure maps to cadastral maps increased markedly as the century progressed.[3]

Maps, by their nature and usage, are bound to disappear. There are numerous archival references to maps lost or only known from later copies. John Lee, a surveyor from Baddow, was employed by Hoare when he bought the New Hall estate at Boreham in 1713. Lee[6] wrote of a map commissioned by Cromwell (when he had the estate) and "in my hands sometime in order to make a new map thereof, according to the present alterations which were many". The maps for Cromwell and by Lee do not exist. The scarcity of maps in a surveyor's long career suggests numerous losses. Twenty-eight years intervene between the making of the first and second surviving maps by Benjamin Agnis of Colchester. He may have been too busy on his farm to have undertaken more surveying, but it is far more likely that his maps have disappeared. Moreover, there are several surveyors who advertised their services but for whom no maps are known. William Beauchamp of Earls Colne thanked "those gentlemen who have employed him in surveying and mapping their estates"[7], but none of his maps are to be

3

found. Just as irritating is the number of maps, often beautifully executed, that are anonymous. The five maps made in 1739–42 of the Essex estates of Wadham College, Oxford,[8] are good examples. There is nothing in the College archives or elsewhere that identifies the surveyor. In short the cartographic record is sadly incomplete, and the fraction lost is substantial and likely to be variable for each surveyor. Undoubtedly many maps remain hidden, their owners perhaps unaware of those interested in their history. Fortunately, 18th century maps of Essex estates are still coming to light and new names are still being added to the long list of land surveyors.

A map may contain the only available information on a surveyor. That Hayward Rush was a writing master and teacher of navigation in 1734 at Wivenhoe and eight years later a land measurer and teacher of the mathematic at Colchester is known from what he wrote on his maps. He made one map with William Kendall who styled himself "Algebraist", another Colchester schoolmaster. The style of their individual maps is similar enough to suggest a link between the two.

Most country surveyors worked in parishes near to their own home. If their residence is not known, then the pattern of surveys will hint at a likely parish for their home. Much archival evidence links the careers of John Coffyn of Great Burstead and his successor William Cole of nearby Ramsden Belhus; the areas that they surveyed are so similar that they had to be neighbours.

One man was usually both surveyor and cartographer. This is clear from formulas like "Surveyed and delineated by James Craddock", "Surveyed and plotted by Richard Sherwood", or "Surveyed and mapt by me, John Lee". A few maps indicate that the cartographer was not the surveyor. An undated map,[9] well decorated in the style of the 1720s, shows the manor of Dovers, Hornchurch, very probably copied from a 17th century map. "Drawn by Ed. Lens" is written on it. Edward Lens was a professional artist and does not figure as a surveyor.

"Amateurs" did have a go at drawing maps. A messuage in Ardleigh was mapped in 1714 "per George Creffield."[10] The Creffield family employed the professional surveyors, John and William Kendall, to survey their lands. George may have been copying such a survey. On his map he drew a house in the conventional manner and then added a plume of smoke rising from the chimney, not a usual addition to professional cartography.

The most pleasing amateur was J. James who in 1742 drew a street map of Plaistow Ward, West Ham, on the back page of his list of local residents and their properties.[11] The map has a verse with it:-

A FUTURE PLEASURE

When old impotent age my limbs has tyed
Infirmity won't let me walk or ride
I can view my country by my fireside.

Of course not every professional land measurement was accompanied by a map. Timothy Skynner listed seven land measurements in an account[12] rendered to Mildmay: only one measurement was followed by a map, the price of the vellum being included in the account. A few surveyors appear never to have made a map. Joseph Butler, of York and then of London, had no maps to his name but he was much in demand as a Commissioner for Enclosures (including the 1778 enclosure of West Horndon) and surveyed the north-west Essex estates of Christ's Hospital.

Maps have to be the prime source of information on who did or did not measure land. Land surveyors were known only from their work. They had no professional register and no corporate identity. Land measurement was the one task that united an otherwise disparate body of 18th century men whose primary occupation was often quite different. Essex land was measured and mapped by London instrument makers and teachers in the City's mathematical

Rococo cartouche by Matthew Hall Jnr. (see p. 120), 1778, with unusual maritime inset.

schools, by local farmers and village teachers; the list includes a coach painter, an exciseman and a bookseller (see Table One).

The term "surveyor" had more than one connotation. Parish surveyors were parish officers who oversaw the maintenance of local roads, a purely administrative job. The evolution of the County Surveyor in 18th century Essex has been described by Nancy Briggs[13] who showed that the office required a surveyor of buildings and bridges with a knowledge of architecture. Land measurement did not come into it. Just as in London the term surveyor described those who surveyed buildings (and valued them) and were often builders and architects. Institutions like Guy's or Christ's Hospital employed such men to look after their buildings and town property but used land surveyors to survey their rural estates. To take an example from Colchester, Isaac Green, alderman and builder, described himself as a surveyor when advertising land for sale.[14] His own lands were measured by a land surveyor, his near neighbour Edmund Plume.

The first professional body of surveyors consisted of 16 London surveyors of buildings, most of them being architects as well. They inaugurated the Surveyors' Club in 1792 at a meeting held in the Shakespeare tavern, Covent Garden. It was not until 1834 that the Land Surveyors' Club was formed at the Old Bell Inn, Holborn.[15]

TABLE ONE

ALTERNATIVE OCCUPATIONS OF LAND SURVEYORS

(excluding land valuation and sale, by treaty or auction)

Auctioneer
J. Storer (Halstead); S. Harvey (Kelvedon); G. Sangster (Brentwood) J. Dew (Brentwood); R. Mundel (Billericay)

Brewer
A. F. Gibson (Saffron Walden)

Carpenter (& timber seller)
W. Jupp (London); L. Searles (London); W. Moore, Snr & Jnr (Ongar) D. Warner (Bishops Stortford); M. Hall Jnr. (Maldon)

Chart Maker
J. Gascoyne (London); J. Friend (London)

Estate agent/bailiff (to a family)
P. Whittington (Brentwood); S. Harvey (Kelvedon); J. Storer (Halstead) J. Wiggins Jnr (Danbury); Hurrell (Boreham); J. Cadman (Aveley)

Excise Officer
J. Wood (Romford)

Farmer
B. Agnis (Colchester); R. Parker (Runwell); B. Fallowes (Purleigh); M. Dayles (Buttsbury); J. Lee (Baddow); G. Hutson (Hutton); E. Plume (Lexden)

Gardeners (Nursery)
S. Driver (London); A. Driver (London); W. Driver (London); G. Sangster, and son, (Brentwood); J. Golding (Brentwood)

Instrument Maker
R. Cushee (London); J. Warner (London); N. Hill (London); T. Heath (London)

Military Engineer
J. Thomas

Painter (of signs)
T. Fort (Witham)

Stationer
J. Dew (Brentwood)

Teacher
J. Fitchatt (Brentwood); J. Vevers Jnr (Romford); W. Pullen (Chelmsford); T. Grout (Fyfield); R. Baker (Terling & Witham); J. Davey (Tolleshunt D'Arcy); E. Laurence (Northants); John Kendall (Colchester); Joseph Kendall (Colchester) (of mathematics); J. Warner (London); J. Ham (London); ?P. Kingsman (London); W. Kendall (Colchester); J. Nelson (Colchester); M. Martin (Epping); R. Wenham (Wivenhoe); W. Cole (Colchester); J. Taylor (Brentwood); H. Rush (Colchester); D. Halls (Colchester); R. Dallinger (Witham)

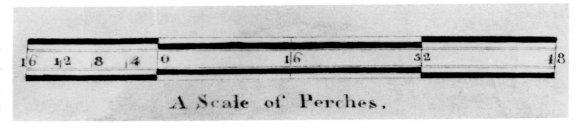

Scale bar by George Hutson (see p. 125), 1777. The "stepped" scale was used by Hutson in all his maps. Scale bars were customarily undecorated at this time.

A Scale of Perches.

Apart from maps, every scrap of archival evidence has been sought to illuminate the careers of land surveyors. Advertisements in local newspapers of the time have proved fruitful, and letters, although few in number, have been revealing. For surveyors like John Storer of Halstead and George Sangster of Brentwood their few surviving maps only hint at careers made obvious from other sources. Too many land measurers remain but a name on a map. Every name has been checked by reference to *The Dictionary of Land Surveyors*, edited by Peter Eden. However it is more than a pious hope to suggest that further research will illuminate that name. Unfortunately land surveyors were not so highly regarded for their contemporaries to leave biographical details. Just as a picture may reveal something of the artist to the viewer, so an estate map will show something of the surveyor.

It is evident from the number of land surveyors and the diversity of their backgrounds that 18th century education must have provided many opportunities to learn land measurement and its associated skills. The large number of Essex schoolmasters who practised surveying suggests that they must have taught the subject to many pupils. Oliver Goldsmith[16] had a true reflection of the times when he portrayed the village schoolmaster ("the village all declared how much he knew") as one who measured land. So, it is appropriate, before considering the work of surveyors, to explore the 18th century links between education and land surveying.

Land Surveying and Education

THE TEACHING OF practical mathematics, including land surveying and navigation, started to spread during the last years of the 17th century and became widely recognised in the first half of the 18th century.[17,18]

Mathematical schools were founded for the prime purpose of educating boys for service at sea. The navy and the merchant marine had a constant need for officers who could navigate. In London, Samuel Cunn, author of textbooks on surveying, headed one such school, and John Ham and Samuel Warner, both of whom surveyed in Essex, taught at a school founded by a physician in order to educate boys for sea service. Among others in Essex, Henry Boad's school in Colchester taught both navigation and land surveying. In Wivenhoe, navigation was taught by Hayward Rush and later by Richard Wenham, both of whom surveyed land in Essex.

Perhaps the best example of these mathematical schools was the one founded by Christ's Hospital, many of the boys being examined by Trinity House to determine their fitness for sea service. A remarkable survival from that school is a map,[19] entitled "The Platt or discription of Oxley Wood in the parish of Gains Coln in Essex as it was taken in the year 1602 and since extracted by one of the mathematical schollers this 30th day of April 1690". The map is a rough but exact copy of a small portion of Treswell's professional map of Colne Engayne which also survives in the archives.[20] The pupil had obviously been set an exercise in computation as he wrote on the bottom of the map "In the lease for Christ's Hospital the wood did let for 22 acres more or less. But Mr Richardson saith it is computed to be 30 acres. And this 30th April 1690 if the scale and plotting be right in the old survey its cast upp to contain 28ª 1ʳ 32ᴾ." Thus the boy learnt the practical necessity of land survey in terms of land value.

The army taught surveying to its officers at Woolwich, where Thomas Yeakell, the Duke of

Cartouche by William Cole, of Colchester (see p. 112), 1783, typical of his use of a rococo frame with chains of flowers.

Richmond's full-time surveyor, was sent to polish up his mathematics. The Duke was not always lucky with his surveyors, his wage book has an entry against one, James Simpson "Ran away Aug. 1766, hanged May 1768".[21]

Schools teaching practical mathematics were set up all over the country, a trend in 18th century education well described by Nicholas Hans.[18] The Universities took no part in this advance. Moreover Dissenters were barred from a university education. So it is not surprising to find that not one of the many Essex schoolmasters who surveyed was educated at Oxford or Cambridge and several of them were Nonconformists. There were three Huguenots who surveyed in Essex, John Thomas, John Rocque and his brother-in-law Bernard Scalé. Benjamin Fallowes of Maldon and Gibson of Saffron Walden were Quakers, the latter taught by a Quaker. Lord Petre, a prominent Roman Catholic, employed a group of local surveyors of the same religious persuasion.

"Mathematics are now become a popular study, and make a part in the Education of every genetleman" wrote Edmund Stone in 1723.[22] He was a gardener's son educated in the Duke of Argyll's household. By the end of the century such a well known school as Oundle had Thomas Dix teaching land surveying and writing a textbook[23] on the subject for his pupils. When, in the 1770s, Robert Dallinger of Witham was advertising his services as a teacher, land surveyor and seller of "all kinds of mathematical, philosophical and optical instrument",[24] he was expecting replies from the local gentry.

A rise in fortune and social scale made a difference. Fitchatt, who owned his own school in Brentwood, sent his son to Cambridge, as did Bernard Scalé when he inherited money from his wife.

The 18th century was the heyday of Essex schoolmasters' making ends meet by surveying and mapping land. The century begins with a highly decorated map[25] of 12 acres only in Roydon by Michael Martin, "Practitioner in Arts Mathematical", and ends with the 1800 map[26] of "All the arable, pasture, meadow, woodlands &c" in Great Oakley "as taken by Wm. Powell, Gt. Oakley, Joseph Harris, Wix, Wm. Piddington, Ramsey, Schoolmasters, and copied by John Allen, Schoolmaster of Gt. Oakley". Excluding this team, Table Two lists all Essex surveyors known to be schoolmasters and all schools known to have land surveying as a subject in the curriculum. The list is large enough to illustrate how easy it was to learn about surveying but is bound to be incomplete. There may be certain overlaps and changes that are not reflected in the list. For instance, two Witham schools had surveying in their curriculum and Dallinger, surveyor and teacher, also lived in Witham. He may have had his own pupils or taught at one of the two schools. Vevers' school at Romford had surveying in its curriculum when Vevers Jnr was advertising as a surveyor. When his name disappeared from the advertisements, the school no longer had surveying as a subject.

Apart from these teachers having had to be taught land surveying, the subject must have been common knowledge. So it was easy for an amateur like George Creffield to map part of his family's land. In the same way farmers like Agnis, Dayles or Hutson could have learned the principles of surveying at school and so taken it up as a later career.

Land owners would have found a knowledge of surveying to be useful in watching the management of their estates. It is not surprising to find that Lord Petre's library[27] contained several books on surveying; the Conyers' library[28] had a smaller selection. However the Honeywoods[29] had no books on surveying but many on horses and horsemanship, as befitted a military family. Local attorneys, who had so much to do with buying and selling land, would also benefit from expert knowledge. Thomas Sewell, a lawyer of Earls Colne, made careful notes[30] of the sizes of new maps if their scale was to differ from the original plan, thus displaying some expertise in cartography.

In summary, education in the 18th century had a strong non-academic but practical concern with measurement of all sorts of down-to-earth items, including the measurement of land and its display on a map. The knowledge had really been available from the last quarter of the 17th century but it was much more widely disseminated in the 18th century. This is exemplified by William Leybourne's books. In 1685 he wrote *The Compleat Surveyor* (which Dallinger[13] bought in a revised edition in 1771) and *A platform for purchasers, a guide for builders and a mate for measurers.* Both of these books were bought by Lord Petre.

TABLE TWO

SCHOOLMASTERS AND SURVEYING IN ESSEX

Key   1. = 1st half of 18th cent.; 2. = 2nd half of cent.
        Surveyors = S. (M = maps known; Ad = advert. only)
        Head of school teaching land surveying = H

NORTH ESSEX

Colchester	Henry Boad, 1. HM: Joseph Nelson, 1. SAd: Daniel Halls, 1. SM: John, Joseph & William Kendall, all 1. SM: Benjamin Rush, 1. SM (also of Wivenhoe): William Cole, 2. SM: J. Strutt, 2. H.
Halstead	C. Brown, 2. H.
Wivenhoe	Richard Wenham, 2. SM. H.
Coggeshall	J. Davis, 2. H.
Steeple Bumpstead	John Buchanan, 1. SAd.
Earls Colne	W. Gilbert, 2. H.
Braintree	W. Sargeant, 2. H.
Saffron Walden	P. Larcher, 2. H. (later at Baddow)
Great Bardfield	John Agar, 2. H.

CENTRAL ESSEX

Chelmsford	William Pullen, 2. SM: John Bowles, 2. H.
Witham	Robert Dallinger, 2. SM: H. Thompson, 2. H: Thomas Allen, 2. H: James Dunn, 2. H.
Writtle	C. Smith, 2. H: Robert Baker, 2. SM. H.
Tolleshunt Darcy	J. Davey, 2. SAd.
Danbury	R. Wilson, 2. H.
Roxwell	D. Gibbon, 2. H.
Fifield	Thomas Grout, 2. SM.
Epping	Michael Martin, 1. SM.

SOUTH ESSEX

Brentwood	Josiah Taylor, 2. SM: John Fitchatt, 2. SM H: de Freis, 2. H.
Romford	J. Vevers Snr, 2. H: J. Vevers Jnr, 2. SAd.
S. Ockendon	H. Bradbury, 2. H.
Billericay	– Levitt, 2. H.
Prittlewell	Henry Bate, 2. H
Thorpe	John Bentfield, 2. H.
Waltham Abbey	John Adams, 2. H.

NOTE: this table excludes schoolmasters named on 1800 map of Great Oakley and listed in text.

The Purpose of Estate Maps

TODAY WE CAN gain a unique detailed view of 18th century Essex through its estate maps. As historical documents they justify Bernard Scalé's claim[32] in 1771 that he surveyed estates "so that the owner becomes perfectly acquainted with the circumstances of his estate, the same as if resident thereon". He was writing for absentee Irish landlords but provided just such a picture[33] of the Mistley estate for Rigby. But in looking at the maps we now can see, in Scalé's words, "at one view . . . the Topographical Appearance of the Whole, the Quantity, Quality and present value of each farm with the exact amount of the Timber on the whole estate".

Thompson, the historian[3] of the Royal Institute of Chartered Surveyors, takes a more prosaic view. For him, the "estate map was but a tool of estate management, and its purpose was to facilitate the fixing and collection of rents and to prevent their suppression and concealment through nibbling encroachments and surreptitious lapses which might otherwise go undetected". This somewhat narrow view rightly emphasises the importance of boundaries. Their importance was explained in 1727 by Edward Laurence, himself a practising land surveyor. In his book, *The Duty of a Steward to his Lord*, he wrote:- "As a steward should know the Quantity and Quality of every parcel of land occupied by the several tenants, so likewise he should have a map of the whole drawn out in the most perfect method; which may show . . . the true figure of every parcel, by representing all the bends in the hedges, or other boundaries thereof, so nearly that he may detect any tenant from alienating the least parcel of any land from his lord."

A much lesser light also emphasised the importance of boundaries. Hayward Rush, a schoolmaster of Wivenhoe, wrote on his map[34] of that parish (1734), "I have endeavoured to be very exact in laying down as well as surveying the boundaries of the parish with its bearings and position of roads, lanes, heaths, woods, rivers, brooks, farms, houses etc. in a very concise manner." He added the somewhat cryptic message, "My greatest care was to let the Truth have the full economy of my survey. Always observing to keep with the verity of Geodesie."

Land owners remained silent on what they wanted from a survey of their farm lands. Family archives are rich in letters from estate owners to the handful of famous landscape gardeners, outlining what they wanted for their parks and gardens. The survey of farms was too much a routine of estate management to deserve specific comment. So the recent discovery of an estate map,[35] dated 1771, is particularly fortunate because attached to it was a letter from the land owner, explaining what he wanted. The map was made by Samuel Harvey, a local surveyor, for George de Horne. The letter states:-

"The surveyor is desired drawing out the map in the table casting up the number of acres to make two columns at the top of which putting their proper titles. One the contents of the land belonging to each field, the other the contents of the improvable arable land exclusive of the fences ponds etc. To get the proper and most usual name of every field of the tenant and sett down the names to note which part of the land or part of a field is copyhold and how much. Colour all the parishes all different so that by a view of the mapp may be seen in what parish each is in or if any lies in two the exact bounds of each parish.

I would not choose to have the map on a large scale but as compact as the accuracy of delineating every curve in the hedge rows and roads and giving the exact and true form of each field will admit – and in each hedge row or anywhere else if any to note the timbers or trees like for timber therein and I hope that it will be done not only in a very accurate but a neat manner".

The requirements laid down in this letter are indeed satisfied by the majority of estate maps. Boundaries are shown most clearly, with lines of various colours to distinguish one property from another. Sometimes a boundary is shown as a "naturalistic" hedgerow. Field names and acreage are commonly put on the map of the field but may be given in the table of contents. The frequency of field names that indicate area (i.e. nine acre field) is a reminder of past measurement, maybe made in "time out of mind". The term "quality" used by surveyors indicated whether the land was pasture, arable, or woodland. This record of land usage was often given in the table of contents but in the second half of the century it was more usual to find it represented on the map itself. Davis, in his textbook[36] of surveying, published in 1798, explained the technique: "Make hedges in Indian Ink and adorn one side with proper shadings or colour to represent ditches. Pasture and meadow to be touched up with transparent green in imitation of grass. Arable or ploughed land with a brown earthy colour in such a manner as will render the same all through a similitude of ridges and furrows." Excellent examples of this technique are to be seen in the Essex maps of Scalé and Mumford, and also in the work of a local Essex surveyor, George Hutson of Hutton.

The occupants of each parcel of land are sometimes named on the map, but more commonly on the tables of contents. Often, especially with larger estates, there was a field book or terrier that gave this information and the map would have numerals or letters referring to these documents. From the archivist's point of view this practice was unsatisfactory as the field book often got lost with time, making it impossible to interpret the surviving map. Such an event bothered the Commissioners of Sewers for the East Greenwich level in 1743.[37] They "observed with great regret" that the only map of the level that they possessed was dated 1697 and that the accompanying field book was lost. "A great inconvenience attending the plan of the old map and which rendered it almost useless was the variety of marks" used as a key to the field book. With that book lost, the map was valueless. So, in employing that busy Essex surveyor, Timothy Skynner, they laid down that the details usually recorded in a field book should be included on the map. He obliged with long tables of contents placed below the map.

The importance of timber as a capital asset to an estate is very clear on estate maps. Jeremiah Nicholls, a north Essex surveyor, seems to have specialised in showing trees on his maps. On a map[38] of a 35 acre farm he drew 556 trees, presumably as an accurate account and not from excessive zeal. Trees in hedge-rows as well as in woods were often shown. The Dagnams estate, near Romford, had 1317 oak trees in 1748 and 752 of these were in hedges.[39] Individual trees were sometimes shown as boundary markers. They figure prominently in the written perambulations of parish boundaries. The great historian of Essex, Philip Morant, wrote of his own parish boundaries, "Over the brook, within Aldham Hall's second meadow at the South East corner an old alder was marked which is now down; therefore a Maple leaning over the brook is marked . . . A little further North an Elm was marked but is now cut down. An oak is therefore marked."[40]

Baroque cartouche by Edward Laurence (see p. 39), 1722.

Many maps list and number trees by species, all being broad leaf trees. The scale of measurement for woodland differed from that of other land. Heath noted "customary woodland measure" on his maps. John Kendall explained on the back of a 1703 map[41] that the woodland measurement of a pole was 18 feet, compared with 16½ feet for the usual pole.

Estate maps displayed essential information on the size, shape, usage and occupancy of the land mapped. More detailed comment on condition of the land or tenants' rights form the substance of written surveys and particulars. Fortunately there are some nice exceptions to this rule. "The salts is a very coarse piece of land yielding little or not profit" wrote E. J. Eyre of London on his map[42] of a Bradwell farm belonging to New College, Oxford. Thomas Alefounder, a north Essex surveyor, made a decorative feature of his list of people "intitled" to mow a meadow, adding that they "must mow down their crop and carry off their hay between the 3rd of May and the first of August". If they missed this time slot then "the tenant of the said farm may prevent them from coming to the said meadow by locking up the gates".

There is romance in the cryptic note made by John Watts of Kent on his 1703 map[43] of the manor of North Shoebury. "The said manor holds and does suit and service to the manor of Kingshill commonly called Wispering Court . . .; which Court is called Wispering at the first cock crowing on the Tuesday after Michmas." The Manor Court of Kingsmill, Rochford, was indeed called the Lawless or the Whispering Court because of a paranoid lord of the manor in the early 17th century. He had returned one night to find his tenants whispering among themselves. Considering this to be threatening behaviour he decreed that henceforth the Manor Court should be held at midnight (the "lawless hour") on the first Wednesday after Michaelmas and that the roll should be called in a whisper.

The essence of an estate map is the depiction of land on a measured scale, In no other way can boundaries and areas be recorded accurately. In criticising some maps[44] Hindley, a Dagenham surveyor, rightly insisted that every map must have a scale bar with a clear statement of the scale used; a scale of chains was not enough, the length of the chain used had to be specified. He also insisted that every map must have a polar indicator. The makers of estate maps did not subscribe to the convention of most printed maps in having north at the top of the page. The lands were fitted in to the rectangle of the estate map in the most convenient manner, and the polar indicator might point in any direction. The 1738 map[45] of Weald Hall in South Weald had north at the top of the page but the 1743 map[46] had north at the bottom, a complete reversal.

Topographical features gradually appeared on estate maps as the years passed. Arable, pasture, marsh, ponds and woods were shown by good drawing and colouring, rather than symbols. Mathew Hall of Maldon claimed to show "all remarkable particulars such as hills, valleys . . . by the rule of perspective",[47] but his maps do not bear out his claim. Printed maps of the time had no accurate way of showing the relief of land. Contour lines were not introduced until the 19th century. Few land surveyors even attempted to show relief; it was not essential to their purpose of recording boundaries and areas. Rocque and his brother-in-law Scalé did manage a satisfactory depiction of relief by shaded colour. Earlier, Edward Laurence, in his maps[48] for Lord Maynard, attempted unsuccessfully to draw the occasional hill. Of all surveyors working in Essex it was only Thomas Bateman of London who drew a realistic three-dimensional picture of land. His map[49] of the chalk pits at Purfleet (1767) gives a clear view of the excavations, which looks odd as the nearby buildings are shown in block plan. Of course this depiction was not suitable for a landscape gardener like Humphrey Repton, of Hare Street Romford, who "found that a mere map was insufficient; as being no more capable of conveying an idea of a landscape than a ground plan of a house does of its elevation".[50] But the purpose of an estate map was satisfied by a two dimensional representation.

The depiction of buildings on estate maps changed as the 18th century progressed. The 16th and 17th century convention of showing buildings in elevation "lying on their backs" continued into the early 1700s. But the accurate depiction of individual buildings by the Walkers of Hanningfield was unique. The buildings shown in elevation or in perspective were symbolic rather than accurate. Gradually this representation gave way to block plan, although churches were still drawn in perspective with some accuracy. Roads were shown as boundaries to land, and not emphasised as routes to travel. "None of the King's Highways are included in this map" wrote John Raven of Terling in 1778.

de Horne asked for a convenient scale on which to set out a map. Most Essex estate maps have a scale of 10 to 20 inches to one mile; only a few go up to the scale of 26.6 inches that was later laid down as the ideal for tithe maps. Convenience of handling the maps seems to have been of little concern to the cartographers. Only George Hutson of Hutton stated that he would produce his surveys either as "sheet maps or in minature in books for the pocket".[51] Many surveyors, such as Mum-

ford of London, produced a large map on a roller and a book of maps for use at a table. Cartographers often produced copies of old maps at a reduced scale.

Maps of Crown estates were usually on paper backed with cloth and mounted on a roller. The Surveyor General's office had invoices[52] such as "paid 16 shillings for 10 rollers", "paid Wm. Wilks, linen draper, for cloth for pasting sundry plans upon £1-0-7", and "paid 7/6 for leather straps for fastening bundles of plans."

Monochrome cartouche by Timothy Skynner (see p. 80), 1764. The difference between this cartouche and that on the Skynner map of Lexden (frontispiece) lends weight to the theory of two Timothys, possibly father and son.

DECORATION OF MAPS

Most, but by no means all, estate maps were decorated. Decoration satisfied a secondary purpose of such maps, for, as Davis wrote[36] in 1798, "it greatly behoves every surveyor to please, if possible, his employer" by putting on decorations because "if the whole be well performed the map will be a neat ornament to hang up in the owner's study . . . so that at leisure he may see his whole estate in his chamber and likewise the particular quantity of each and every enclosure without any manner of trouble but rather a pleasure".

Obviously the "working surface" of the map was no place for decoration, although Thomas Holmes populated his fields with men and animals (map[53] of Quendon, 1702). In the first decades of the 18th century much use was made of several highly decorative scripts for the map title. The skills of the earlier writing masters were also shown in decorative line patterns. Most cartouches were then full of colour and provided a somewhat heavy framework for titles. An achievement of arms added further colour and complimented the land owner. A large pair of dividers, often very well drawn, was usual above the scale bar, which itself might be surrounded by decoration. Heavily decorated borders to a map were fairly common. Types of leaf and flower design in the border would complement the floral decoration around the framework of a cartouche. Big coloured compass roses were also a common feature.

As the century progressed, the framework of cartouches came to be drawn in black or sepia, and the design changed from baroque to the lighter rococo style. The influence of Adam on so much design from moulded ceilings to mirror frames was obvious in the decoration of estate maps. Scripts became more simple and were modelled on the clear "type-face" letters used on contemporary engraved maps. Around 1775 the cartography of estate maps reached a peak of excellence. The clear and informative layout of the "working surface" was enhanced by fine penmanship and the good use of colour to illustrate the ploughed ridges of arable land and the green pastures. Adamesque cartouches or titles set on classical ruins in a sylvan scene were executed with considerable artistry. Scale bars were now plain, and polar indicators either plain or decorated with drawings of farm implements or more fanciful conceits. By the end of the century the estate maps had become more prosaic and much like the "clean" outlines of the contemporary engraved county maps.

The artistic competence of land surveyors varied from the laughably bad to the finest expression of Georgian artistic taste. Most men stuck to a style that was recognisably personal but within the common contemporary themes of design. A few were more versatile and tried out several styles; John Raven of Terling was such a man. When the maps of a surveyor cover many years it is possible to show a development of personal style, usually conforming to the changing fashion for decoration.

An anonymous map[54] of two very small farms in Debden and Broxted drawn in 1768 for a minor land owner has a poor cartographic rating in terms of the skill shown in delineating the "working surface" but is quite remarkable for the beauty of its decoration. The title is set in a rococo frame set in to a sylvan scene with sheep grazing by a stream and backed by classical ruins. Each corner of the map has an exquisite shell decoration and above the scale bar is a luxuriant bow of ribbon. The whole appearance suggests that the decorations were done by a hand that was not that of the cartographer or surveyor.

There is good evidence to show that not every map was decorated by the surveyor himself. Peter Kingsman's bill[55] for his 1729 survey of Ashlyns manor (near Bobbingworth) includes the item "Paid the painter for writing and decorating the survey". In 1766 the land surveyor, *Drakeshill Farm from a map of lands in Navestock by Edward Laurence, 1722* William Cole, and the artist, J. Dunthorne, both of Colchester, advertised[56] that they would work together in the business "each attending to that part of it which is particularly adapted to his profession". They added that "Perspective views of particular places will be inserted if required." John Johnson of Suffolk had the cartouches of a 1777 map of his survey painted by his artist son William. A year later Jupp and Dugleby, both of London, got the artist William Tomkins to write and decorate a map of their West Ham survey. An advertisement[57] by a London firm of surveyors in 1788 stated "Maps & etc. beautifully embellished by the most eminent landscape painter." Finally, James Taylor's map[58] (1791) of Southchurch has pasted on to it a water colour picture of boats on a shore.

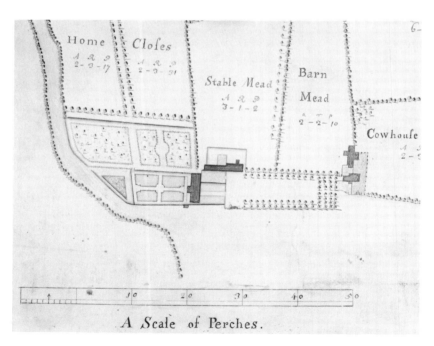

A Scale of Perches.

The Work of a
Land Surveyor

LAND MEASUREMENT

AUGHT IN SCHOOLS and practised by schoolmasters the measurement of small land areas was scarcely the focus of 18th century technological advance. The mathematics, techniques and instruments required had all been developed by the time of Queen Elizabeth's death.[59] On the other hand the measurement of a whole country by triangulation had to wait upon invention and new engineering of instruments. William Roy,[60] begetter of the Ordnance Survey, knew his instruments were inadequate for his survey of Scotland in 1747–52. He called his map of Scotland "rather a magnificent military sketch than a very accurate map of a country". He proposed a survey of all England in 1763 but the device to measure the long (27404.72 feet) base at Hounslow (across Heathrow Airport) was not perfected until 1784. The measurement of angles from that base could not be started until 1787 when Jesse Ramsden delivered his newly designed and unique theodolite.

"There are but two material things to be done in the field, the one is to measure the lines, and the other to measure the quantity of an angle included by these lines", wrote Laurence in 1726,[61] adding that the handling of the necessary instruments, like the art of fencing, could not be taught from a book. Distance was measured by a chain, the length of a cricket pitch, invented by the astronomer Edmund Gunter in 1620. The chain had 100 links to be used in measurement, and ten chains measured a furlong (220 yards). The man "leading" the chain carried ten small stakes, called arrows, putting one down for every chain's length measured.

Angles were measured by a circumferentor or with a theodolite. Leonard Digges' Elizabethan theodolite was not bettered until Sisson's model appeared in the 1720s. It was a sophisticated form of circumferentor, but both instruments needed a bulky tripod for firm support.

The mid-18th century has been called the golden age of the chain surveyor. Surveying by the chain was the most common method used as it entailed the minimum of apparatus. The field, or fields, was divided into convenient triangles by staking out the lines to be measured. The distance between each of the three points of a triangle was measured with a chain, and so no angular measurement had to be made. The lines were drawn as near as possible to natural boundaries and the exact position of these could be measured by offsets at right angles to the line. A cross-staff, with two peep sights set at right angles, was used for alignment of offsets.

For larger farms it was more appropriate to use a theodolite and to measure around the outer boundary. The line of each chain measurement was determined in degrees from magnetic north (the apparatus contained a compass). A complete 360 degrees brought the surveyor back to where he started. This is called a closed traverse or transit. The middle of the farm could be surveyed by open transit, laying lines and offsets at a measured number of degrees from the initial boundary measurements. The sophisticated method of triangulation

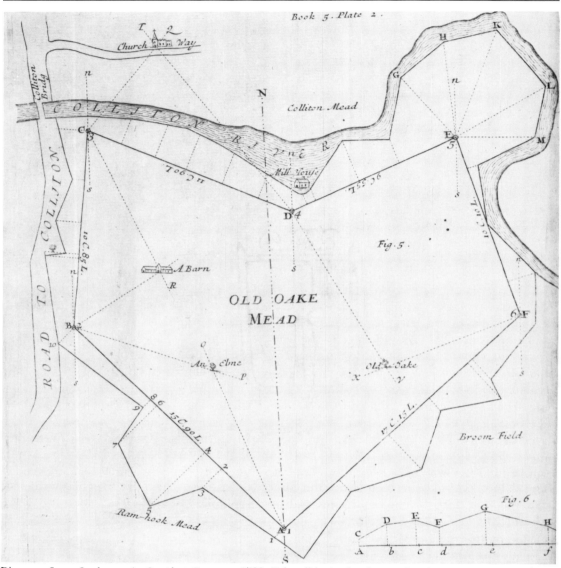

Diagram from Leybourne's *Compleat Surveyor*, 1722 (5th edition), showing a closed traverse survey using a circumferentor.

Having chosen suitable landmarks the surveyor sets up his instrument at station A, sighting on station B. The angle between the line A–B and north is measured (the position of north is shown on the compass mounted in the circumferentor). The length of the line A–B is measured with a chain with 100 links. The measurement is made in parts to allow measurement of sets off to the irregular boundary of the field. Each set off is at right angles to the line A–B (the angle checked with a cross-staff). The process is repeated at station B, sighting on station C, and so on, until station A is sighted from station F. The position of other landmarks is determined by angulation from two stations. The data are recorded in the conventional surveyor's notebook, set out below. The angles can be expressed by the quadrant of the compass (as in this example) or in degrees clock-wise from north. Linear measurement is in chains (C) and links (L).

Remarks	Sets off	Station line	Sets off	Remarks
	C-L	A. NW 43° 30′		
	0-70	0-0		
	1-51	4-43		At station A the elm
	4-30	5-30		tree bears NW 20° 0′
Ram	3-05	9-10		
Brook Meadow	0-65	10-0		
	1-40	15-90		
		B. NE 7° 30′		
	0-85	0-0		
	A gate	2-10		At station B the elm
	1-95	3-85		tree bears E 60° 0′

And so on throughout the survey

could be used for estates. In this only the base line of a triangle is measured, and the angles between each end of the base and the lines connecting the third point are measured. From this the length of the lines can be calculated, thus saving a lot of chain measurement. Whatever method was used the area of the land measured could be calculated from the size of the triangles.

It is obvious that a land surveyor did a lot of walking on his job. He had to inspect the whole estate, noting the natural features and finding the places where he could stake out his triangles or set a transit line. He would learn about the farm from the farmer. James Carter,[62] who as a schoolboy assisted William Cole of Colchester, remembered the hospitality of the farmers "at whose houses we took up our abode while measuring their lands". Even though Cole surveyed "within a circle of about twenty miles from his residence", "when the grounds were large and there were more than an ordinary number of difficulties in working quick it was necessary to spend three or four days in measuring the estate". During this time the farmer could provide information on land use, the names of neighbours and special boundary marks. "To taking an account of all the fields in the Island and making out a list of how they were cropped" is an item in the accounts of Mathew Hall of Maldon. This must have been done with the help of the farmer.

Land measurement could not be done by one pair of hands. Carrying and setting up apparatus and staking out the points from which measurements were to be made took time and manpower. Chain measurement obviously needed a man at either end of the chain. Carter wrote of Cole, "He wanted someone to draw the chain and to do other little things which a boy could easily perform." Rigby hired three unskilled assistants to help Scalé in his large survey[63] of the Rigby estates. It was more usual for the surveyor to do the hiring and charge the client. Skynner's charges for assistance were so varied that it is probable that some assistants were more skilled than others. Accurate chain measurement did require skill. For a survey of Thurrock Thomas Browne, a well-known surveyor, had as his clerk or assistant James Crow, who was himself a land surveyor. The written record[64] labels Browne as "Esquire" and Crow as "Surveyor". It is easy to guess who did the leg work.

The skill of land measurement lay in the correct calculation of area for irregularly shaped fields and the optimum choice of lines and angles of measurement to allow an accurate representation of natural boundaries. There seems to have been little dispute by clients about the surveyor's accuracy. When Skynner came down from north Essex to survey Greenwich marshland his clients checked the accuracy of his survey by getting another surveyor to measure a sample of the marsh.[65]

The size of any commission to survey varied enormously. If a client employed a surveyor to come from afar, then the survey was likely to be of a large area. It was obviously more economical to have a local surveyor for measurements of small parcels of land. Often these small surveys were not mapped. Hall surveyed two meadows in Maldon and just recorded the area. After a re-measurement of a small farm he made alterations to the old map. The local surveyor was called in to measure changes in field patterns and boundaries. In this role Mildmay employed Skynner, both living in Moulsham, and Strutt employed Raven, both of Terling.

The expertise of land measurement could lead to a surveyor being asked to check another's plans. Skynner went up to Bedfordshire to see how a change in the turnpike road would affect an estate he had surveyed. "I walked with the chief surveyor" he wrote[66] "and set forth to him I thought if the road was carried thro sixteen acres it would be . . . a vast deal less expense . . . and less damage considerably done to the estate."

The work of the land measurer was more physical than intellectual. With some feeling Henry Wilson, dedicating his book[67] on surveying to Edmund Halley, pointed out that the astronomer's great "Acquirements" had advanced him "to a station of much more honour and less toil than that of a practical surveyor". Martin Nockolds of Saffron Walden "wanted an active man" when he advertised[68] for an assistant who "understands land surveying and can plan with accuracy". In common with civil engineers and country attorneys, travelling from job to job was a burden for the land surveyor. Then, as now, English weather was a frequent hindrance to work. No wonder Hugh Jones of Billericay asked[69] clients to have their land surveyed in October: the harvest was in and the weather likely to be fine. Winter was not good for the land measurer. "The lands are so wet and heavy and the days so short that I cannot proceed" wrote[70] Storer of Halstead in December 1781. The next November he wanted to survey "whilst the weather is free from snow".[71]

An odd hazard faced Lee of Baddow when surveying the foreshore at Prittlewell. A horde of men landed from Kent to take the oysters. "When I measured the shore the chain was drawn between their legs." He had the satisfaction of producing his foreshore map in court when these men were prosecuted.[72]

OTHER WORK AND OTHER PEOPLE

*L*OOKING BACK AT the 18th century, Thompson,[3] the historian of the Institute of Chartered Surveyors, considered that "The image of the surveyor as a man whose activities ended up in a map was prolonged, and even overshadowed the branching out into valuing, management and property dealing which was going on at the same time." This hindsight seems unduly coloured by the views of the 1830s when the newly formed Land Surveyors' Club objected to the Tithe Commissioners' rates for parish valuation and survey on the grounds that "persons qualified in the profession for surveying and mapping, and to whom an allowance of two guineas a day would be ample remuneration, are not of sufficient experience to value, and that the said allowance is not adequate to ensure the employment of persons of respectability and experience for the careful and proper valuation of tithes". A snobbishness born of the determination to become a profession, a 19th century concept. "Land surveyor" was not a nice term for James Beadel, a Chelmsford man, who in 1846 announced that he was a surveyor and auctioneer, as "land surveyor implies the measuring of land; a surveyor generally implies the inspection and valuing of property".[73]

The gathering together of activities that became the expertise of the 19th century chartered surveyor is not apparent in 18th century Essex. Then individuals with their personal expertise offered a variety of skills to those who employed them for the maintenance of country estates. Land surveyors, estate managers and some lawyers were all concerned without the constraints of professional bounds, or formal qualifications. It must be remembered that Elizabethan surveyors were gentlemen who had the Latin necessary for the understanding of the law relating to land tenure; many estate maps of that time were drawn for use in legal disputes. It was in the 17th century that land measurement became an occupation for artisans.

Two outstanding gentleman-surveyors worked in Essex early in the 18th century. Edward Laurence wrote extensively on estate management, agriculture and land measurement. He advised clients on all these subjects and valued land. His high reputation is indicated by his one Essex patron being Lord Maynard, for whom he surveyed in Essex and Leicestershire. It is significant that 30 years later Maynard employed Timothy Skynner, a local artisan surveyor who was essentially a land measurer. The other worthy was Thomas Browne, a Herald and a surveyor much in demand as a valuer of land and an expert on tithes. One example of his work indicates his skills. In 1749 Sir Bibye Lake's estate in West Thurrock had to be divided after his death into four equal portions. A Commission "issued out of the High Court of Chancery" was formed, its four members being landed gentry, headed by Champion Branfill of Upminster. The Commissioners then appointed Browne as the surveyor because he was "of great experience in the Valuation of Estates". The estate was inspected in the company of Caleb Grantham Esq., the estate manager who owned property nearby, and Mr Sumpner, a carpenter, who had worked on the buildings. Brown surveyed land and houses, produced a map and an account of the tithes. The final meeting of this rather grand commission of the High Court of Chancery was held at the Dog and Partridge in Stifford, a nice reminder of rural life.[74]

The catalogue of people involved in a major survey is obviously easier to find in official records than in family archives. However it is likely that the land surveyor would have the estate manager with him and both would interview tenant farmers. The survey itself was to provide accurate information for future estate management. For example, in 1778 the Worshipful Company of Embroiders[75] discovered that their estate in Stifford was neglected. The "very ancient names" of the tenants dated back 150 years and there were "alterations made by dividing the fields". To put things to right they employed Bernard Scalé as the surveyor, presumably because he had shown his ability as a land measurer, valuer and agent for sale or purchase of estates. A committee of the Company visited the estate with Scalé, who had been given an old map by a tenant's solicitor. Land and buildings were inspected; they found Stifford Hall "a very small and contemptible building". In the end the Company was well pleased with Scalé's work as it gave "pleasing hopes of considerable future benefit".

To set against these few land surveyors who could be considered to have been totally employed in the role of a chartered surveyor are the great number of Essex land measurers who did just this throughout the 18th century. In the 1770s Robert Dallinger, a Witham schoolmaster, whose advertisements outnumbered his maps, made no mention of valuation or estate sale when listing his accomplishments in land and timber measurement, making and copying maps. Valuation was also omitted in George Hutson's advertisements. He combined a busy career as a land measurer with farming at Hutton. A. F. Gibson of Saffron Walden, advertising as a land surveyor "after having served a regular apprenticeship with a person of eminence in that profession", made no claim beyond that of land measurement and mapping, adding "Old plans reduced to any scale and copied in the most approved style". This was in 1786 when William Cole of Colchester, another schoolmaster, was engaged in a great deal of land measurement without entering into the other aspects of what became the work of a chartered surveyor.

But, at this time, things were changing in London. By 1767 E. J. Eyre, a London land surveyor of considerable reputation, had put on his maps of the Essex estates of New College Oxford "Survey'd, Valued and Plan'd".[76] Down from York to London came Joseph Butler, a land surveyor who apparently never made a map. Christ's Hospital employed him in 1783 to help solve a dispute about tithes in their Essex estates.[77] The Hospital's governors had already obtained a counsel's opinion on the matter and then told the treasurer to appoint a "skilful person to examine the hospital's tithes and lands . . . and that an estimate of the same be prepared". Joseph Butler made a survey, but the maps of this were not made by him. In the same way he had been a Commissioner appointed by the private enclosure Act obtained by Lord Petre for enclosing land in West Horndon.[78] Butler always dealt with the more legal aspects of land ownership.

The law and the land are seen more clearly in the local context of 18th century Essex. One indication of the interdependence of lawyer and land surveyor is the large numbers of 18th century estate maps which have been presented to the Essex Record Office by Essex solicitors. In his book[79] *The Attorney in 18th century England*, Robson took several examples of Essex attorneys to show how much they had to do with estates. Most of the stewards of manorial courts were attorneys, and one would hold the appointment in several manors. William Mason of Colchester is cited as such a man. Most of his work was concerned with land valuation and sale. The account books of T. F. Gepp,[80] an attorney of Chelmsford, itemise countless journeys to view estates and to deal with tenants' problems. It is probable that Dawtrey of Kelvedon Hatch had his attorney and not his local land surveyor draw up the "particulars" of an estate in Wickford that he purchased. "Upon the whole this estate is so improvable and lies so convenient for the sending its produce to London market either by water or land carriage that it cannot be worth less than 26 years purchase at £100 per annum."[81] Later John Luther, Dawtrey's great-nephew, employed a local land surveyor, William Moore, to measure his Essex lands but had Aske of Needham Market, Suffolk, to guide him in the law and the management of his estates.[82] Writing in 1775, Aske apologised for a delay in his work, "being appointed by one of my best friends Under Sheriff for the county". He went on to state that "I have been into Essex and made a valuation of a farm . . . at Much Easton" and "shall go to Sussex in the summer and see crops on the ground". He told Luther to "avail himself" of the full value of his lands. Of a difficult tenant he wrote "You will save yourself much trouble if you are peremptory with him and the rest of your tenants. It is in the nature of the farmer to complain, whether his bargain is beneficial or not." Aske clearly would value, view and advise without recourse to a land surveyor.

An excellent example of similar work performed by a lawyer or a land surveyor is provided by two documents[83] in the archives of St Thomas' Hospital, London. The title of both is "A particular of several farms belonging to St Thomas' Hospital in Essex, Cambridgeshire and Buckinghamshire". The first version, dated 1774, is by John Yeldham of Bardfield Saling, Essex, an attorney. He made a very detailed survey, commenting on the state of husbandry and reliability of the tenant farmers. The second version, dated 1781, is by Joseph Freeman, a Cambridgeshire land surveyor who also mapped in Essex. His description is almost the same as Yeldham's but he added the acreage of each field and stated that the farms were now under his inspection.

Yeldham was himself a man of substance, living in a "good brick house" and owning several properties in Essex. He managed the very considerable Essex estates of Guy's Hospital and was steward for the estates of Jones Raymond of Saling Hall and for Lewis Way in Dunmow. For the county of Essex he was a Deputy Lieutenant and also Receiver General. This indicates the sort of prominence reached by a local attorney, which can be compared with that of a land surveyor like Timothy Skynner, who surveyed for Raymond and Way and so was under Yeldham's orders.

The attorney who inspected estates was most probably using measurements and maps provided by a land surveyor. Of course, some land surveyors would do the whole job themselves, including making a new map. This is what the ubiquitous Thomas Browne did when writing up the particulars of Hugo Meynell's estate in North Ockendon.[84] He valued this estate at £30,573-1-10 (note the odd shilling and ten pence). "This estate", wrote Browne to Richard Benyon of Gidea Hall, "is without exception better tenanted and better paid than any estate in the county." Benyon showed the particulars to his banker who advised purchase. Benyon's lawyer did the conveyancing.

Estate valuation was not the prerogative of the attorney or of the land surveyor. A few gentlemen, usually agriculturists, became estate valuers and consultant estate managers. Their surveying was in terms of the land's quality rather than its area. Such a man was Nathaniel Kent of Fulham. His retirement was marked by Norfolk farmers who gave him a cup "in token of their respect and esteem for his integrity and impartiality between landlord and tenant in his profession as a surveyor of lands".[85] Some years earlier Kent[86] had drawn attention to William Black as one of "the best judges of the nature and value of land". Black, who just styled himself as gentleman, lived in Epping but worked from the Middle Temple, although he was not a lawyer. He advised Lord Braybrooke of Audley End, the Houblons of Hallingbury Place and Sir Robert Lawley on the value and management of their estates.[87]

When in 1793 the Chelmer and Blackwater Navigation Company started work, its founders required a surveyor skilled in land valuation, as they had to buy land for the work.[88] They asked Black to become the Company's surveyor, but he refused on the grounds of conflict of interests, as he was adviser to some of the local land owners concerned. John Joscelyn of Ipswich was appointed. Although he called himself a land surveyor he was known, like Black, as a valuer. When land had to be measured it was done by Matthew Hall of Maldon but Joscelyn then did the valuation. Similarly if Rennie, the consultant engineer to the project, wanted land measured or mapped he called on Hall. For a special building such as Beeleigh mill several people were called to value it. Joscelyn valued first but when this was disputed Hall, Rennie and Constable were called in. It is a short tale of who did what. Hall was a carpenter/timber merchant with a sideline in land surveying. Rennie had started as a millwright before becoming a leading civil engineer, and Golding Constable was a mill owner and father of the artist John Constable.

A gentleman in the mould of William Black was John Wiggins of Maldon who advised Strutt and others on their estates. Unlike Black he may have measured land. Certainly his son did,

Elaborate "double cartouche" with table of symbols and surveying instruments from the title page of a book of maps of the Barrington family estates by John Mackoun (see p.69), 1766 (see also illus. p. 34)

and made maps. Another gentleman was James Wright of Woodham Mortimer.[84] For the purpose of tithing he made a written survey in 1791 of the 1200 acre estate in Writtle and Roxwell belonging to New College Oxford. The next year he made for the College a terrier of some of these lands when they were leased to Daniel Blyth. Unlike Yeldham he does not appear to have been a lawyer as he did not represent the College in a tithe dispute settled in the Chelmsford court. He did deal in land, being associated with Parker, the well known estate agent of Chelmsford. He also figured as trustee to a surgeon's estate in Baddow and for some other land in that parish, having as co-trustees such distinguished gentlemen as Bramston and Strutt. Wright died in 1795, leaving his oyster layering in Paglesham to his son.

By the second half of the 18th century most local Essex land surveyors were dealing in the lease and sale of property, usually in conjunction with an attorney. Several surveyors became auctioneers and did not confine their auctions to property. George Sangster auctioned wine and, from his Brentwood nursery garden, once sold deer.

John Storer of Halstead appears to have been the only local surveyor who went into estate management, for Lord Nugent and Sir Thomas Spencer-Wilson. But Storer did everything, dealing in property and offering mortgages on the security of land. In 1790 he went into partnership with an auctioneer who was a cabinet maker, upholsterer, dealer in British wines and deputy agent for the Sun Fire Office. In addition Storer surveyed and sold timber. The pair must have made quite an impact on the local land owners.

The movement towards the combined skills of the modern chartered surveyor was perhaps better seen in London with the formation of what would now be called a consortium. There is no evidence to show the success of this rather anonymous process, but two advertisements that appeared in the *Chelmsford Chronicle* indicate what was on offer. The first, in 1771, was from Heath and Dodson, land surveyors to be addressed at Old Slaughter's Coffee House, St Martin's Lane. They would "accurately survey, plan and value estates; take levels for the conducting of water; draw perspective views plans and elevations in architecture; value and measure timber; ascertain the quantity and quality of the different sorts of soil contained in any farm and its value per acre; also direct the method of improving those lands; inclose plant and divide common fields and lands intended to be improved". Presumably they were planning to employ a whole team of experts to do these many jobs. Much later, in 1788, Maddocks & Co. of Grevil Street, London, did not offer such a wide range of services but were trying to drum up business. "The Nobility and Gentry are respectfully informed that a Gentleman who is one of the actual surveyors of his Majesty's forests and other lands, purposes to attend on Monday, Tuesday and Wednesday following at the White Hart Colchester during which days he will be at leisure to contract for any estates to be surveyed valued bought or sold or let or to advance any sum or sums of money on good freehold security. NB Maps of estates etc. beautifully embellished by the most eminent landscape painters on very moderate terms." The last note is a clear reminder that all the decorations on a map were not necessarily put in by the hand that made the map. As to the identity of the gentleman surveyor, it is anyone's guess, but Joseph Pennington ought to be a front runner.

SOCIAL STATUS AND INCOME

S EVERAL ESSEX MEN must have derived their status (and much of their income) from their business and not their surveying. Land measurement was a secondary occupation for Matthew Hall with his Maldon timber yard and for George Sangster selling plants from his Brentwood nursery garden. Fitchatt owned his own school in Brentwood, and only a few surveys are by him. George Hutson's obituary called him land surveyor and farmer.

Judging from the whole of the Essex scene the land surveyors who worked in that county fitted in to the varied and variable pattern of middle-men, sandwiched between the few at the top and the multitude at the bottom of Georgian society. The Essex experience confirms Dr Porter's excellent analysis set out in his book *English Society in the Eighteenth Century*.[90] Land surveyors, wherever they worked, depended on the landed gentry. In turn, these gentlemen needed, in Porter's words, "the services of a penumbra of bailiffs, attorneys, clergy, surveyors, mortgage-brokers and horticulturists." Apart from the role of the clergy and attorneys (for conveyancing) the land surveyor could supply some of the services of the others mentioned.

Land surveyors in Essex were individualists, exploiting their own talents and connections. They did not yearn to become members of a corporate body, defining or controlling the work they did. Yet, as Porter points out, they formed one of the groups who "became haunted in the nineteenth century by the quest for professional security and status". What brought about this change of attitude is outside the scope of a review devoted to the 18th century, in which there were instances of increasing professionalism but not a detectable mass movement. In the 1790s Robert Baker turned from running his school to a combination of land surveying and teaching and went into the 19th century to found with his son a business that dealt with surveying, especially for parish authorities and public bodies like the Turnpike Trust, with valuation and sale of property, not to mention the giving of advice on agriculture. Parish surveys led up to the huge volume of work for surveyors imposed on them by the Tithe Commutation Act of 1836. It cannot be a mere coincidence that the Land Surveyors' Club was founded in 1834 and formed the basis of the Society of Chartered Surveyors.

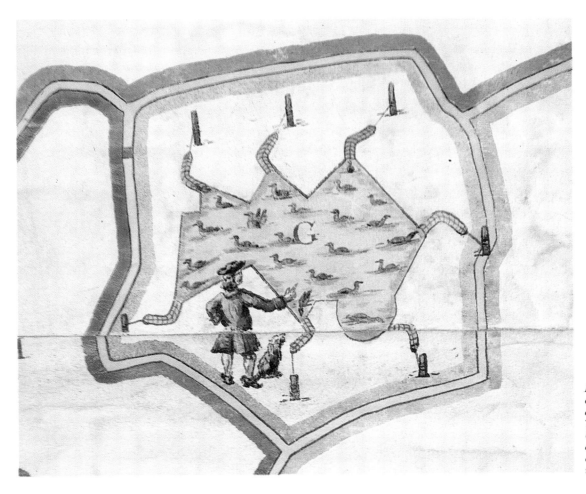

Decorative interpretation of duck-decoy from an an anonymous map of Tillingham, 1739. Unusual industrial or agricultural features often tempted map-makers into illustration.

In the 18th century a man was a gentleman or yeoman by birth and not by achievement. P. B. Scalé, although born of an impoverished Huguenot family, was declared a gentlemen by virtue of the family connections, long before his success as a surveyor. His brother-in-law and fellow Huguenot, John Rocque, became one of the best known London cartographers but was never a gentleman. Many of the London surveyors were urban artisans, like Crow, who started with Thomas Browne, gentleman, but continued a successful career with Marsh, a fellow artisan. William Cole of Ramsden Belhus was named a yeoman throughout his life but distinguished himself as a local surveyor.

Country attorneys and manorial stewards (often one and the same) must rank above land surveyors, who depended upon them for work. The attorneys also made more money. The measurement of land was not a road to riches. Timothy Skynner, as busy a local Essex surveyor as one could find, managed to buy a very small property near Chelmsford only by raising a mortgage.

It is difficult to compute the income to be derived from land surveying in those times. Throughout the 18th century it was the custom of surveyors working in Essex to charge sixpence an acre surveyed. Presumably this charge was as much as the land owner would pay, and his decision is likely to have been influenced by the rental value of his land. Yet when rental values increased rapidly in the last 15 years of the 18th century, local surveyors such as William Cole of Colchester and Isaac Johnson of Woodbridge, Suffolk, were still charging only sixpence an acre. Even that rate was undercut, at fourpence per acre, by Hutson, who farmed in Hutton, and Hall, who owned a timber business in Maldon. Both these men must have derived a good income from their alternative work and thus could afford to charge a low rate for their land measurement.

It was still difficult for surveyors to get the full price for the job. There was an acrimonious correspondence[91] in 1803 between George Alston, an attorney acting as agent for Edward Blair of Little Horkesley, and William Cole. On the completion of a parish survey (presumably of Horkesley; no map exists) Cole had put in a bill for £70-2-6. Alston objected and offered £20. "I am as much averse to litigation as Mr Blair or any other person can be but I am equally averse to Imposition" wrote Cole, adding "The bare mention of £20 I can consider in no other light than an insult." In the end Cole was paid £57-15-0.

Piece-rate work must have tempted the surveyor to make the quickest survey that would still satisfy the client. Dr Eden[92] has suggested that an average day's survey would be 20 acres, the charge for this matching the day rate of 10 shillings charged by some Norfolk surveyors. This estimate would fit in with John Heather's 1725 map of 20 acres "surveyed on Sept. 28th". Sherwood mapped 949 acres, "surveyed in May and June", which works out at 20 acres per working day.

It is somewhat surprising to find that William Fairbank,[93] much in demand as a Sheffield surveyor, was only charging five shillings a day in 1757. By contrast, in 1765 Thomas Yeoman[94] charged a pound a day for surveying part of the river Chelmer, but he was primarily a civil engineer. A fascinating bundle of accounts in the Public Record Office[95] shows that in the 1790s surveyors working for the Surveyor General on Crown land charged £2-0-0 a day. Land measurement alone produced less income than surveying for tithing. A memorandum[96] written in 1805 by the incumbent of the parish of Great Tey recorded that William Cole of Colchester "has sixpence an acre for surveying and mapping, and his expenses". However "Mr Wiggins of Danbury surveyed and set the tithes of Great and Little Horkesley at seven pence an acre", and for this service in the parish of Mile End Colchester charged tenpence an acre.

A good example of surveying to resolve tithe disputes comes from the archive[97] of Christ's Hospital. The Governors decided in May 1783 to solve their problems with a new survey of their large estates in north-west Essex. The survey was made by Joseph Butler, who had come down from York to set up business in London. He presented his completed survey on 7 April

1784, and charged £650-0-0 for his work that had taken him ten months. This was a considerable sum, far more than could be earned from simply measuring land.

The Essex experience suggests that a land measurer could earn around £156-0-0 annually. Valuations and other work would increase the income significantly. Comparable Essex incomes of the time would have been £20 for a farm labourer at the top rate, £30 for a carpenter and £105 for a millwright, the highest paid artisan.[98] Colquhoun's estimates,[99] based on the 1801 census, give £200 per annum as the average income of persons "employing professional skill . . . as engineers, surveyors and master builders of houses". Land surveyors in Essex were certainly able to earn around that average, but with considerable individual variation. Many, of course, had other sources of income.

PRINTED COUNTY MAPS

*I*N MAKING THEIR manuscript maps land surveyors used the cartographic conventions, scripts and decorations established on printed maps. But surveyors had little to do with the very different world of the trade in printed maps.

In the first half of the century land owners could, and did, obtain up to date manuscript maps of their estates but had to make do with county maps printed from altered Elizabethan copper plates. The trade was in the hands of cartographers and engravers who shamelessly copied from one another, leading to "the little esteem or rather great contempt that maps are in here."[100] It was a time when versions of Saxton's 140 year old maps could be sold as the best available county maps by George Willdey at "The Great Toy Spectacle Chinaware and Print Shop". Many additions and corrections were claimed but these were not really significant. The only real change was the inclusion of roads taken from Ogilby's surveys of 1675.

It was not until the middle of the century that completely new surveys of whole counties were made and mapped on a scale of one or more inches to the mile. This work was in response to popular demand (and financed by subscriptions) and encouraged by prizes given by the Royal Society of Arts. This was a new field for the land surveyor, who often was his own publisher.

Three names are pertinent to Essex. Isaac Taylor of Ross surveyed his native Herefordshire in 1754. He went on to make more county surveys and was a prolific estate surveyor in the south-west, particularly in Dorset. His work must not be confused with that of Isaac Taylor of Brentwood, who in 1755 surveyed some local lands and then became a London engraver. He was the forebear of another Isaac Taylor who, at the end of the century, lived in Colchester and did engrave maps. William Yates, a customs officer of Liverpool, surveyed Staffordshire in 1769. His maps were engraved by John Chapman and published in 1775, when the pair proposed a survey of Lancashire. Yates was also a busy estate surveyor and came to Essex in 1794 to survey for Bamber-Gascoyne, whose Lancashire estates he also surveyed. Yates was the only surveyor of counties to make a significant estate survey in Essex. The first large scale map of Essex was made by John Chapman, land surveyor and engraver from Dalham in Suffolk.[101] His Essex survey, from 1772 to 1774, was undertaken with Peter André, a Huguenot.

The minimal connection between Essex estate maps and the cartographers of the trade in printed maps has a strong Huguenot flavour. John Rocque, the most famous Huguenot in the London map trade, mapped a small farm in Essex belonging to Tylney of Wanstead House. But Rocque had previously published engraved plans of the gardens of that house. His brother-in-law and fellow Huguenot Bernard Scalé made the most beautiful maps of Rigby's estate at Mistley. Scalé had been taught by Rocque when they were both in Dublin. Most of Scalé's work was in Ireland, but he had family connections in Colchester, married an Essex girl in Dedham and came back from Dublin to live near Warley in Essex. There he prepared his *Hibernian Atlas* for publication in London.

The well known 1777 large scale maps of Essex by John Chapman and Peter André preserved the Huguenot connection. According to Gough (1780)[102] "John Chapman, land surveyor, began in 1772 for Mrs Rocque a map of this county." Mary Ann Rocque was Scalé's sister and carried on her husband's business after he died in 1763. Peter André was a Huguenot, a close friend of John Rocque and a witness to his will. John Chapman's first map, of Newmarket in c.1765, was supported by subscriptions to be collected by Mrs Rocque. His short career (he died in 1778) was mainly concerned with large scale county surveys. His one surviving estate map[103] is of a small parcel of land in Orfordness, Suffolk.

His one Essex estate map was of the parish of Beaumont cum Moze and is known only from the will of the incumbent, Rev. Robert Dingley, who left it to his successor to dispose of as he thought fit.[104] Dingley probably used Chapman's survey of the parish when he challenged the Governors of Guy's Hospital on the extent of their estate in the parish. The Governors refused to tell him how many acres they owned.[105]

There is a short tailpiece to the story of Chapman's county map of Essex. Prior to his survey, Thomas Sparrow, a busy land surveyor from Hammersmith, announced[106] in June 1769 that he proposed to survey the county of Essex and invited subscriptions. Of the three people willing to receive the subscriptions, one was Mrs Rocque. Sparrow, who had just published a printed plan of Colchester, proposed that his map would be on a scale of two inches to the mile. A month later he announced that the scale would be changed on the grounds of economy to one inch to the mile. This is the reverse of Chapman's proposals, which were for a scale of one inch, later changed to two and a half inches to the mile for his published maps. After a long silence, Sparrow was in print again in December 1769, thanking those who had paid subscriptions and announcing the return of the money as he had engaged to go abroad next April. In fact the year 1770 saw him down in Dorset surveying the Lulworth Castle estates.[107]

References and Notes (Part I)

Catalogue marks refer to documents in the Essex Record Office unless indicated otherwise.

1 E. Lynam; 1947. Foreword to *Catalogue of Maps in the Essex Record Office*.

2 A. C. Edwards & K. C. Newton; 1984. *The Walkers of Hanningfield Buckland Press, Dover*.

3 F. M. L. Thompson; 1968. *The History of Chartered Surveyors*.

4 See A. F. J. Brown; 1969. *Essex at work*. ERO.

5 A. Young; 1807. *General View of the Agriculture of Essex*.

6 See *Essex Review*; 1942. *51*, 205.

7 Advertisement in *Chelmsford Chronicle*; 1776.

8 Original maps in Wadham College, Oxford (copies T/M 303–7).

9 Map D/DU 186/2. Bernard Lens and his son, also Bernard, were well known artists of this time. Their names and that of Edward Lens are in the list of subscribers to Le Clerk's book on architecture published in 1723. All three are described as "lymners". There are two Essex examples of an amateur draftsman not being the surveyor. "J. Wise del". is written on a crude sketch of Ashingdon parish (D/DU 300) used for the perambulation of 1797. "Drawn by Robert Simms" is on a poor map of a farm (D/DE1 P8). These two men were obviously not artists and no more is known of them.

10 D/DR P26.

11 D/DPe M55. Loose in this book is a rough copy, made by James in 1753, of a 1624 map of a West Ham manor.

12 D/DMy 15M/60.

13 Nancy Briggs; 1984. *Architectural History. 27*, 297.

14 Advertisement in *Chelmsford Chronicle*.

Cartouche by William Cole of Ramsden Belhus (see p. 54), 1720 showing his characteristic style of decoration: a single pen line filled with blocks of bold colour (cf. illus. p. 129).

15 These details were obtained from the Library of the Institute of Chartered Surveyors.
16 O. Goldsmith; 1770. *The Deserted Village*.
17 E. G. R. Taylor; 1966. *Mathematical Practitioners of Hanoverian England*. Cambridge.
18 N. Hans; 1966. *New Trends in Education in the 18th Century*. London.
19 Map in Guildhall Library.
20 Map in Guildhall Library.
21 See R. A. Skelton; 1962. *Geographical Journal*. 78, 416.
22 Quoted by E. G. R. Taylor; 1971. *The Haven Finding Art*. London.
23 T. Dix; 1799. *Treatise on Land Surveying*.
24 Advertisements in *Chelmsford Chronicle*.
25 Map in Map Library, British Library.
26 D/DQs 16.
27 D/DP Z4.
28 D/DW Z8.
29 D/DQs 40.
30 TB 186/12.
31 The ERO's copy of this book has on the fly-leaf "R. Dallinger 1771".
32 P. B. Scalé; 1771. *Tables for the Easy Valuation of Estates*.
33 D/DF1 E1.
34 D/DU 27.
35 D/DU 893/1.
36 W. Davis; 1798. *A Complete Treatise of Land Surveying*.
37 From the Minute Book of the Commissioners of Sewers, Greenwich, in the GLC Record Office.
38 D/DU 155.
39 D/DNe E10. A written timber survey by T. Davis.
40 Transcribed from *Essex Parish Records*; 1950. ERO.
41 D/DWe P5.
42 Map (1768) in New College, Oxford.
43 D/DS 120.
44 Hindley's commentary on the copies of maps by Yates is in the archives of the Marquis of Salisbury.
45 D/DTw P1.
46 D/DTw P2.
47 Advertisement in *Chelmsford Chronicle*, 1776.
48 D/DMg P1.

49 D/DZn 4.

50 From *The Works of the Late Humphrey Repton*. ed. J. C. Loudon; 1840.

51 Advertisement in *Chelmsford Chronicle, 1778*.

52 In Public Record Office (CRES 2/1602).

53 Original map in private hands (ERO T/M 170).

54 D/DCn 46.

55 Kingsman's bills are in the Library of the Royal College of Physicians.

56 Advertisement in *Ipswich Journal*.

57 Advertisement in *Chelmsford Chronicle*.

58 D/DBz P2.

59 See A. W. Richeson; 1966. *English Land Measuring*. MIT Press.

60 See Y. O'Donoghue; 1977. *William Roy*. British Museum Publications.

61 E. Laurence; 1726. *The Young Surveyor's Guide*.

62 Quotations from his *Memoirs of a Working Man*; 1845.

63 D/DHw A2.

64 From the Chancery Court Records in the Public Record Office.

65 From the records of the Commissioners of Sewers in the GLC Record Office.

66 From a letter in the Bedfordshire Record Office.

67 H. Wilson; 1762. *Surveying Improved* (5th edition).

68 Advertisement in *Chelmsford Chronicle*, 1794.

69 Advertisement in *Chelmsford Chronicle*.

70 D/DFr A3/5.

71 D/DFr A3/6.

72 Details taken from the *Essex Review*, 52, 38.

73 The quotations are taken from F. M. L. Thompson, Op. cit. (ref. 3).

74 Documents in the Chancery Court records in the Public Record Office.

75 From the Company's Minute Book in the Guildhall Library.

76 Original maps in New College, Oxford (copies in ERO).

77 From the Minute Book of Christ's Hospital in the Guildhall Library.

78 D/DP E47.

79 R. Robson; 1959. *The Attorney in 18th Century England*. C.U.P.

80 D/DGy 5.

81 D/DFa E44/1.

82 D/DFa E44/19.

83 From the records of St. Thomas' Hospital in the GLC Record Office.

84 D/DBe E8.

85 See the *Gentleman's Magazine* for 1811.

86 From N. Kent; 1775. *Hints to Gentlemen of Landed Property*.

87 See C. Shrimpton's thesis (1965) and related documents in ERO, including Black's advice to Guy's Hospital on land values.

88 Details taken from the Company's letter book in the ERO.

89 Facts on James Wright kindly supplied by Miss Caroline Lane of New College Oxford.

90 R. Porter; 1982. *English Society in the 18th Century*. Penguin Books.

91 D/DDt E3.

92 Personal communication from Dr Peter Eden.

93 See T. W. Hall; 1932. *The Fairbanks of Sheffield*.

94 D/DM Z3/5.

95 Documents (CRES 2/1602) in Public Record Office.

96 D/DPb Z5.

97 See ref. 77.

98 Figures taken from A. F. J. Brown, Op. cit. (ref. 4).

99 Tables quoted by R. Porter, Op. cit. (ref. 90).

100 Quoted by G. R. Crone; 1966. *Maps and their Makers* 3rd edition. Hutchison.

101 For details of Chapman's career see A. S. Mason; 1983. *Romford Record 15, 7*.

102 R. Gough; 1780. *British Topography*.

103 The map is in the Ipswich.Museum.

104 Information kindly supplied by Mr J. Bensusan-Butt.

105 From the Minute Book of Guy's Hospital in the GLC Record Office.

106 Advertisements in *Chelmsford Chronicle*.

107 These maps are in the Dorset Record Office.

PART TWO

The Land Surveyors

Two surveyors at work with theodolite and measuring rod: decorative detail from map of Pebmarsh by Hollingsworth, 1807.

Arrangement of Text

THE FOLLOWING ACCOUNT of land surveyors working in Essex is divided into three periods of time, the years 1700–34, 1735–69 and 1770 to the end of the century. Inevitably the first period will contain the last works of surveyors who flourished in the 17th century, and the last period will include the first works of those who became established in the early 19th century. The career of some surveyors is long enough to span more than one of these artificial time periods. When this occurs the whole career will be described in the section devoted to the time period of the initial career, but with the necessary references to the later time period. The exception to this rule is the occasional surveyor whose main career was presaged by one map made in a much earlier year; the time period chosen here will be that which encompasses the main career.

Within each of the three divisions of time the surveyors are grouped according to their known or postulated place of residence. Those surveyors who came in to Essex to work are grouped according to the county of their residence. Thus there is a large group of London-based surveyors and groups in the counties that border Essex (including Kent). There is an interesting group of those who are known to have come from afar and an assortment of those whose residence cannot be traced and who may well have moved about the country, put together in a sort of geographical limbo.

Surveyors resident in Essex are grouped according to the part of Essex in which they lived. A surveyor known only for his maps of a small area of Essex and without record of any work outside the county is assumed to have lived near the area surveyed. The county has been partitioned into north, central and south Essex by two lines drawn east to west. Thus, the north portion runs down from the northern county border to a line running from the north border of East Messing to Little Hallingbury. The central section runs from below this line to a line drawn from the north shore of the River Crouch to the lower part of the parish of Waltham Holy Cross. The southern portion runs from below this line to the southern border of the county. The major towns are Colchester in the north, Chelmsford in the central and Romford in the south portion of the county.

The work of all the surveyors, including the major anonymous surveys, can be seen in relation to these three sectors of Essex. In short, the time/place scheme should indicate who did what for whom, and where and when it was done.

Polar indicator by Thomas Browne (see p. 33) from a map of Navestock, 11726. The simple geometric style and bright colouring were soon to be superseded by more imaginative styles (see also illus. pp. 35 and 128).

31

FIRST PERIOD (1700–34)

Surveyors from outside Essex

LONDON BASED SURVEYORS

THIS GROUP IS divided into those whose prime business was land surveying and those who also had another occupation, such as instrument maker or teacher of mathematics.

An undated map[1] of woodland in Greenstead, near Colchester, is the one surviving Essex survey of JOEL GASCOYNE, chart maker turned land surveyor. Gascoyne was one of the 17th century chart makers who worked beside the Thames, were visited by Samuel Pepys and were freemen of the Drapers' Company.[2] Comberford, Hack and Thornton are the best known names in this school of chart makers who all shared many similarities in style. Gascoyne, the son of a sailor from Hull, gained his freedom of the Company in 1676. He made charts until 1691 when he turned to land surveying and started at the top by surveying the Hertfordshire estates of Lord Salisbury.[3] He then had a spell in the west of England but returned to London in 1700, mapping the parish of Hackney in 1703.[4] He died in 1705, so that his map of Greenstead is likely to have been made between the years 1700 and 1705. The manor of Greenstead was owned by Lord Lucas, so it appears that Gascoyne was not short of powerful patrons. To travel up from London to Colchester to survey just 53 acres would seem an unlikely waste of effort and suggests that other surveys for Lucas may have been done. The Greenstead map is remarkable for its bright crude colours for the cartouche of abstract design with a lion's head at the top. The style is reminiscent of the cartouches drawn by the Kendall family of Colchester but, more important, Hack used the same style on some of his charts. Gascoyne's cartouches for his Hertfordshire map and his Hackney one are sophisticated classical pen drawings, but he used a quatrefoil design for his compass rose for his Essex and his earlier Hertfordshire maps.

In the Drapers' Company JOHN FRIEND was apprenticed to Gascoyne and gained his freedom in 1689. His only Essex work was "A Trewe and Perfect Platt" of the manor of Laindon Hall ". . . drawn by John Friend".[5] The style and content of the map make it clear that it is an unrevised copy of a lost Walker map made a century before.

HEBER LANDS was probably based in London as he surveyed only in the home counties. A sketch plan of a house and grounds in Wanstead is attached to a legal document dated 1712.[6]
Illustration, Back cover The heavily gilded points of the compass written on the four sides of the plan contrast with the plain drawing of the plan itself. In 1720 he went a little further from London to survey Sir James Lumley's two manors in Burstead. The map[7] has a heavily decorated border of conventional foliage and a fine classical cartouche with the Lumley arms above it. It would appear that Lands was more of an artist than he was an informative cartographer.

THOMAS CLEER was another surveyor who worked in the home counties but also worked for the Bishop of London. In 1696 he published two versions of a map of the city of Norwich. His one Essex survey was of the manor of Church Hall, Kelvedon, made for the diocese of London in 1701. The map[8] is curiously in two sheets mounted one on top of the other on a roller. The first page has the title and date but the scale is on the second page and under it is written "Measured and a scale by me Thomas Cleer". The map was added to by Cleer, who put on two parcels of land "as measured this April 1703". The map was well used as, in another hand, there is reference to a timber book made in 1803. Therefore it is curious to find in the Mildmay archives a copy of this map made in 1792 by John Prickett, land surveyor of Highgate.[9] Prickett made a very exact copy in Cleer's style but with a most delicate cartouche of his own in the best late 18th century style. A point of interest is that both maps are accompanied by a certificate signed by a diocesan official on 29 April 1704 to approve the map as a true and accurate survey. This can only mean that Cleer produced two copies of the original map and both were certified. Much later Prickett must have made a copy of one of Cleer's maps and affixed the original certificate to his own work. It would not have been unique for the diocesan authorities to have asked Cleer to provide two copies of his original survey. The minute books of the Commissioners of Sewers, Greenwich levels, show that they demanded a copy of Timothy Skynner's map of the level, and, when he provided it, it was certified as a true survey in the same wording as used for the map he produced first.

THOMAS BROWNE was one of a pair of land surveyors who worked in Essex to gain an entry in the *Dictionary of National Biography*. It is likely that his eminence as a herald (he became Garter King of Arms in 1774) rather than his skill as a surveyor brought him an official biography. Born in Derbyshire in 1702, he entered the London scene as a protégé of John Warburton, herald, cartographer and somewhat disreputable purveyor of antiquities.[10]

Browne, perhaps because of his youth, does not appear to have had anything to do with Warburton's map of Essex, Middlesex and Hertfordshire first published in 1726. Warburton used Payler Smith as the surveyor and Joseph Bland to collect the subscriptions, which were first invited in 1720. The map was completed in 1725. Both were described as "gentleman". Payler Smith made some measurements with the Rev. T. Luffkin outside Colchester in 1722 (quoted by Morant) and Bland surveyed an Essex glebe in 1737. The fact that Browne's early career involved major surveys in Essex and Hertfordshire may have had something to do with Warburton's influence.

Browne's Essex career started at the top, surveying only for prominent land owners and areas of over 700 acres. He surveyed and mapped Lord Waldegrave's estate at Navestock in 1726[11] and the Chigwell estate of Sir Joseph Eyle of Gidea Hall in 1727.[12] This map was made at the end of the year, as he put on it "Blanch Lyon, Pursuivant of Arms", an appointment made on 9 October 1727. In 1733 he surveyed the manor of Blunts in Buttsbury.[13] This *Illustration, page 31 and 128* manor, with the splendid alternative title of "Ging Joyberd Laundry", came from the Bayning family to the Lennards on the marriage of Elizabeth Bayning to Francis Lennard. These three *Illustration, page 35* maps are very attractive with elegant baroque cartouches; two serpents are nicely entwined on the cartouche of his Buttsbury map. As might be expected from a herald, his achievements of arms are well executed. There are two inserts on his Navestock map, one showing Navestock Hall, well drawn in elevation, the other showing a plan of Morden farm. The main part of the map shows buildings in block plan, an early use of this convention.

Browne's next work in Essex comes well into the second time period of this text. In 1749, by order of the Commissioners appointed by the High Court of Chancery, he surveyed the West Thurrock lands of the late Sir Bibye Lake to ensure their fair division among the inheritors.[14] Browne had with him as clerk or assistant James Crow. Both stated that they lived in the parish of St Andrew, Holborn. Crow later made major surveys in Essex, working with Thomas Marsh. Browne stated to the Commissioners that he "for many years past hath been employed or concerned for persons in the surveying and valuing of estates . . . in many different counties in England". He also stated that "he very well knows the nature or kinds and values of estates in the county of Essex". The Commissioners called Browne "an able and experienced surveyor of land . . . and of great experience in the valuation of estates". Browne produced a map and two versions of a field book which included a list of tithes.

Browne surveyed the manor of Wrabness in 1751, as now shown on Prickett's "redelineated" map of 1797. His last Essex work required some detection and much regret of

33

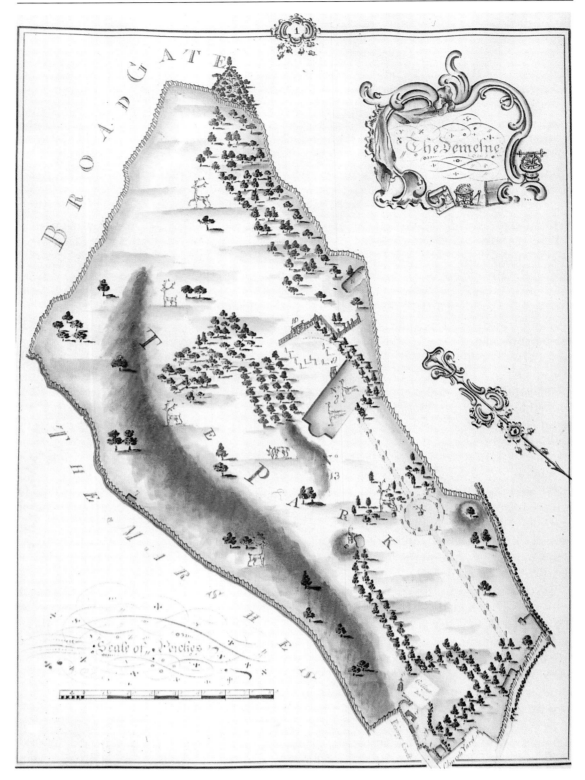

The demesne of Barrington Hall, Hatfield Broad Oak from a volume of maps of the Barrington family estate by John Mackoun (see p. 69), 1766. Note the swans with reflections and deer in the parkland (see also illus. p. 21).

the lacunae in the Benyon family archives. Richard Benyon purchased Hugo Meynell's huge estate in North Ockendon and surrounding parishes in 1758 (the banker's draft for the purchase is dated 23 December of that year). An undated "Field Book and Particular"[15] of the estate gives a detailed description and valuation with the conclusion that "this estate is without exception better tenanted and better paid than any estate in this county." An undated letter[16] to Benyon from his financial adviser makes it clear that Browne was the surveyor: "Our friend Mr Browne came to me this day and showed me the particulars of Mr Meynell's estate." In Browne's particulars every parcel of land is numbered, "the same being expressed in the map or plan of this estate". There is also a note to the effect that "the plan of this estate is at N. Ockendon." Whether this plan was an old one or a new map made by Browne is unclear. A letter[16] from Browne to Benyon, sent to his house in Grosvenor Square, has written on its back "Mr Brown's map of North Ockendon, 20 June 1759". Browne wrote "I am ashamed not to have sent you the enclosed sooner. The plan will be finished next week and will send that and ye old one to Grosvenor Square, but I have ordered a roll and ledge as a large frame is only cumbersome . . ." This implies that Browne made one large decorated map for display in Benyon's town house; he may well have left a series of "working maps" at North Ockendon. The surviving maps of the estate are anonymous and undated. Two maps[17] at a scale of 20 inches to the mile suggest that they formed part of a series on that scale which covered the whole estate. There are also five maps,[18] stitched together, called "Reduced plans of the N. Ockendon estate", but these do not cover all the lands. Finally there is a well bound book of neatly drawn maps,[19] eleven in all, that cover the estate and Benyon's lands in Newbury, Ilford. This volume has "C. Sleight. Delint." There is nothing to indicate that Sleight was a surveyor and no other work by him is recorded. Certainly he was a neat draughtsman, copying the "reduced plans" of the estate already quoted. These plans were almost certainly from the old plans made prior to Browne's survey, as they show Sir Nathaniel Wright as an adjacent land owner and he died in 1737.

Unfortunately Benyon's archives for his Gidea Hall estate do not throw any light on the Ockendon maps. There is an "Account of the fields and rents"[20] of Gidea Hall dated 1766 that refers to estate maps, but no maps are to be found. Benyon had bought Gidea Hall in 1745 and, as noted, Browne had surveyed the Chigwell estate of the Hall's previous owner in 1727.

It would be pure speculation to suggest that Browne also surveyed Gidea Hall and that Benyon had these maps and therefore asked Browne to survey the North Ockendon estate.

Browne lived on until 1780, owning a house in Bedford Row, London, and his wife's original home at Essenden, Hertfordshire. Apart from these two houses he left the sum of £25,000 in his will. This would justify his nickname of "Sense Browne" that distinguished him from Lancelot "Capability" Brown.

AUGUSTINE HALE, probably a London surveyor, was another associate of Browne's. In 1733 the huge Knebworth Hall (Hertfordshire) estate was "Surveyed by Augustine Hale and examined by Thomas Browne".[21] Hale's one Essex contribution was a sketch map[22] of 15 acres in Hockley, drawn in 1706 for Christ's Hospital.

The arms of the Waldegrave family on a map of the family lands in Navestock by Thomas Browne (see p. 33), 1726. This form of decorative compliment to the landowner went out of fashion after 1750 (see also illus. pp. 31 and 128).

Instrument Makers and Mathematicians

The London makers of globes and mathematical instruments used by navigators and surveyors were closely related to the City's mathematical schools. JOHN WARNER, who made these instruments at the King's Arms and Globe, Lincoln's Inn Fields, was most probably a close relative of Samuel and Henry Warner, who taught mathematics. John Warner styled himself "Citizen of London" and for New College, Oxford, surveyed[23] their Suttons estate in Hornchurch in 1717. The estate had been surveyed 54 years previously by John Coffyn of Great Burstead, Essex. It is interesting that the College did not employ William Cole, Coffyn's local successor, to make the survey. The new survey may have been necessary following the breaching of the river bank at Dagenham in 1707. Warner records on his map that he could not survey the marsh "by reason of the mud and water occasioned by a breach of the Thames", but "Mr Bayns who lived upon the skirt of Havering" remembered the marsh to be about 20 acres.

RICHARD CUSHEE and WILLIAM WYETH both worked at the Globe and Sun, Fleet Street. Cushee was an instrument maker with John Coggs as his partner; Wyeth may well have been a draughtsman attached to the business. Cushee, advertising[24] his instruments, added "estates surveyed; maps drawn and engraved". Two of his Essex maps are known, the first only from a 19th century copy. The copied map[25] is of a survey for the Childs family of Ruckholt manor, Leyton. The manor had been bought from Benjamin Collier, who had purchased it in 1720 and had it surveyed in 1721 by Thomas Archer, a local surveyor. It is odd that Cushee should survey it again in 1728. A farm in Berden owned by Christ's Hospital is shown on a 1732 map,[26] "surveyed and drawn" by Cushee. It is remarkable for its spare clarity with a script like a typeface.

Wyeth made two maps of the Eastbury level, marsh land in Barking. The first[27] (1735) showing 1500 acres was drawn by him. The second[28] (1737) of a few parcels of land was "accurately taken by" Wyeth, suggesting that he was the surveyor. The first map has a conventional classical cartouche and the second has the title written on a "mantle" very akin to that of John Noble's contemporary map of land in Barking. Both Cushee and Wyeth worked extensively outside Essex. Wyeth may have died by 1742 when his map of Barking was copied by another instrument maker, NATHANIEL HILL, who also surveyed another bit of land for Mrs Weldale for whom Wyeth's first survey was done.

Both the London teachers of mathematics who surveyed in Essex gave their address as Great Kirby Street, Hatton Garden. There, a mathematical school "for qualifying boys for sea service" had been established by Frederick Slare, MD. Dr Slare (1647–1727) was a distinguished London physician with a love of experimental science that was uncommon among the doctors of the time. His connection with a school is not mentioned in his biography[29] but is to be found in the edition (1733) of Samuel Cunn's Euclid, edited with additions by JOHN HAM, who did survey in Essex. The first map of Ham's was not discovered until 1986, to be followed a year later by another of his maps being presented to the Essex Record Office. These two estate maps of Essex are his only known cartographic works. The first,[30] dated April 1727, was of Elsenham Hall, Ham describing himself as "Teacher of the Mathematics", the second,[31] of April 1728, is of the Broadoak estate in Wimbish and records Ham as "Professor of the Mathematic". His promotion was probably due to Samuel Cunn leaving the Hatton Garden school to take over Neale's school in Fleet Street. Certainly Ham quotes Cunn as his predecessor in his own text included in his edition of Cunn's book. Ham was not an artistic cartographer; his symbolic trees were occasional green splodges.

SAMUEL WARNER was also in the Hatton Garden School, together with his brother Henry who did not survey in Essex. Samuel Warner surveyed[32] in 1733 a 580 acre estate in Arkesden belonging to Richard Cheke, a London apothecary who was treasurer of Christ's Hospital. As the hospital had employed Cushee to survey in nearby Berden in 1732, it is somewhat surprising to find its treasurer hiring a different surveyor. Warner, like Ham, was not an artist. His rather clumsy classical cartouche is topped by an odd-looking boar's head. He put "mathematician" after his name.

It is curious that this pair of London teachers should make their small contribution to Essex surveying by working in the north-west corner of the county.

PETER KINGSMAN is known only for his work for the Royal College of Physicians.[33] That he was a Londoner is clear from his charges for the 70 mile journey from London to Kent to survey the 50 acres at Burmarsh given to the College by William Harvey. That he was not primarily a land surveyor is suggested by the unusual number of assistants he employed and his use of an anonymous hand to make the maps of his surveys. As Dr Slare had been a trustee of the Ashlyn's Manor estate donated to the College by Baldwin Hamey it is possible that Kingsman was another teacher of mathematics at Slare's Hatton Garden school.

Kingsman charged the usual sixpence an acre for surveying the 358 acres of Ashlyn's Manor (near Bobbingworth). His invoice, dated 15 April 1729, contains some unusual items. "Lodging for myself and my horse and the wages of two men and three boys for 14 days" indicates the employment of more people than normally required by a land surveyor. He "paid the painter for writing and ornamenting the survey". The map itself, noted by Gough in 1780 as being displayed in the College, is anonymous and well decorated in the style of the time, with a heavily ornamented border and the arms of the College and of Baldwin Hamey. Kingsman had paid five shillings for "research in the Herald's Office for two coats of arms". He also arranged for the map to be framed and glazed. The same hand made the map of Burmarsh in 1731.

Kingsman went down to Ashlyns in June, 1729, for an eight-day timber survey, employing a carpenter as his assistant. Many carpenters were capable of doing their own survey of standing timber and few land surveyors would have considered getting such skilled assistance. A further point suggesting that Kingsman was not primarily a surveyor of land.

MEN FROM KENT

D R HULL OBSERVED[34] that, up to the year 1700, several Kent surveyors crossed the Thames to work in Essex, but for an Essex surveyor to work in Kent was quite exceptional. This holds true for the years 1700–34, during which no Essex surveyor appears to have worked in Kent.

JOHN HOLMES of Eltham mapped[35] a farm in Hadleigh in 1709, "being the inheritance of Sam Micklewright" who may well have also come from Kent. Holmes travelled further in 1724 to survey[36] the manor of Wimbish Hall (594 a.). The title of this map is written in over-large Roman capitals in lieu of a cartouche. Holmes had been in Essex in 1696 to survey Thomas Abdy's estate in Layer Marney, decorating the map with the Arms of Abdy. But when in 1719 Sir Robert Abdy wanted some of his Essex estate to be surveyed he employed a local surveyor, Benjamin Fallowes of Maldon. JOHN WATTS "of Thornham, Kent" mapped[37] 277 a. in North Shoebury, "actually surveyed and delineated in August 1703". This was an area where two local surveyors, Coffyn and Cole, were active.

At first sight it is strange to find Caius College, Cambridge, employing a Kent surveyor for their north Essex estates. JOHN CRIPPEN, "surveyor resiance in Canterbury" made four maps[38] of the College's farms in Great and Little Bentley, Frating and Great Bromley in 1731. The maps have inset drawings of the farm houses and the borders are lettered to give a grid reference. Although this device was used by John Norden for his Essex map of 1594, it is not necessary on estate maps where each parcel of land is usually numbered or lettered and referred to in a table of contents.

Crippen was probably a member of the Canterbury school of surveyors then headed by Jared Hill. Crippen's maps in the Kent Record Office were made for a clergyman but he never worked, as Hill did, for the Canterbury Cathedral authorities[39]. It is probable that he was chosen by Caius College because the peripatetic Master of the College was Sir Thomas Gooch, later Bishop of Ely. In 1730, the year before Crippen's commission, Gooch was made a Canon of Canterbury Cathedral.

The last of the men from Kent raises a matter of confusion. The 1735 map[40] of the manor of South Hall, East Tilbury, owned by the Wardens of Rochester Bridge, has on it "Survey'd by C. Stoane". There is no other work attributed to a surveyor of this name. The Wardens were in the habit of employing Kent surveyors for their Thames-side Essex estates. At the time they were employing for their lands in Kent a well known Kent surveyor, C. Sloane. Comparison of Sloane's work with the "Stoane" further suggests that it was Sloane who surveyed the land in Tilbury. A close look at the Tilbury map shows the near identity of the letters "t" and "l". The word "Salts" on the map has an unlooped "l" with a large top serif which is very like the high cross line of the "t". All these facts make it virtually certain that there was no such surveyor as Stoane and that the surveyor and maker of the Tilbury map was actually the Kent surveyor, C. SLOANE.

Cartouche by William Brasier, 1730 in a distinctive personal style of 'tube' and entwining flowers. By 1734 Brasier (see p. 40) was describing himself as "Land Surveyor to His Grace the Duke of Montague". (see also illus. p. 90)

FROM NORTH OF ESSEX

To THE WEST of Essex, Hertfordshire did not provide a surveyor in Essex during this time period. While some Essex surveyors travelled up to Suffolk, the only Suffolk man to touch Essex was JOHN CLARKE who in 1722 surveyed Sir Robert Barnardiston's large estate that straddled the Suffolk–Essex border. The huge map[41] has a crudely coloured cartouche. The plain scale bar with divider is boxed in a coloured square that has, at each corner, a cherub head with winged neck. The distinctive feature is the wide printed paper border pasted on to the vellum. This patterned strip was probably a dado for a contemporary wallpaper. Land usage is shown by lettering the fields A(arable), P(pasture), and M(meadow).

A Norfolk surveyor, THOMAS BECKET of Foulsham who surveyed in his native county from 1730 to 1745, made the unlikely trip to Barking in 1734 to map[42] Isaac Leheup's estate. Leheup was described as "of London" by James Turner, a local Suffolk man who in 1723 mapped Leheup's Suffolk estate in Beyton. No explanation for Becket's journey is offered.

Two surveyors have been placed as men of Cambridgeshire, as that was the scene of their major works. JAMES GOULD worked on the St. Thomas Hospital estates in that county.[43] He made a large map, in 1721 of three farms (603 a. in total) that comprise almost the whole parish of Little Coggeshall. The cartouche, in grey wash with no added colour, incorporates two female figures in a complicated formal design that includes a shell design and "foliage". Only 14 years later Skynner made a copy[45] of the map, "as measured by Mr James Gould in 1721". Skynner employed his own style of decoration, but the content of the map is a true copy. As both maps still exist, one can only presume that Peter Du Cane who owned the farms had asked for a copy "Redrawn by Tim° Skynner".

ARTHUR FROGLEY is placed as a Cambridgeshire man because of his extensive work in that county on the estates of the Honourable Corporation of the Sons of the Clergy.[46] Founded in 1678 for the purpose, as Frogley put on one of his maps, "For ye reliefe of poor widows and children of clergy-men", this Corporation held large estates in several counties and was in the habit of employing surveyors local to the estate surveyed. For the Corporation Frogley surveyed[47], in July 1714, a farm in Hatfield Broadoak. The only decoration on this map is the classical pillars supporting an arch to frame the table of contents. His other Essex contribution is an undated map[48] of 28 a. in the parish of Ramsey, belonging to a local freeholder. The map is undecorated and rough in execution.

Frogley's map of Hatfield Broadoak was later copied by J. Newton of Chancery Lane. The copy retains the original title, including "Surveyed by A. Frogley 1714", and Newton's name is written at the bottom of the map.[49] Newton copied many maps for the Corporation (Frogley's Cambridgeshire maps of 1716 and 1719 included) and also for Charterhouse. All these copies were made around 1805–10. This point is laboured, as J. Newton appears in the *Dictionary of Land Surveyors* as an 18th century surveyor. This erroneous entry derives from a map of the parish of Haverhill which has "Surveyed 1737" in the title and at the bottom of the map "J. Newton, del. Chancery Lane". The map is drawn by Newton on a reduced scale from an anonymous survey[51] of 1737 mapped on six sheets, one of which is now missing. J. Newton did survey in Essex in the early 19th century but he had a brisk business in copying 18th century maps.

Northamptonshire produced two widely travelled land surveyors. From Stamford Baron came EDWARD LAURENCE who used a London accommodation address; "he is to be heard of when in London at Mr Senex's at the Globe in Salisbury Court".[52] John Senex, geographer to the Queen, was prominent in the printed map trade which usually had little to do with estate surveyors. Like Thomas Browne, Laurence was a gentleman who won entry to the *Dictionary of National Biography*. He taught mathematics and: "in winter and at such times he is not surveying Gentlemen may have their sons and daughters taught accompt." He was also an estate agent, agriculturist and author of two books, on surveying and estate management, written for the Duke of Buckingham's stewards. For the Duchess he surveyed[53] some land in Little Leighs.

With such a reputation, it is odd to find that Laurence surveyed[54] a 58 acre farm in Navestock. The map is neat and workmanlike, setting out land usage and value, and listing 1660 trees according to species. More in keeping with his career was his massive survey[55] in 1730 of the "Several Estates belonging to . . . Lord Maynard in the Counties of Essex & Leicestershire". Only the Essex maps survive, together with the title page. Bound in a volume of daunting weight the seven maps show 4500 acres of land in Easton, Broxted, Canfield, Dunmow and Thaxted. Maynard's bigger estate in nearby Ashden was not surveyed until 1759 by Timothy Skynner, a local surveyor who also worked for Maynard in Suffolk (Laurence died around 1740).

Illustration, page 11

Laurence's maps for Maynard eschew colour. The cartouche of the title page is in grey wash with a baroque design that incorporates two surprisingly adult cherubs. Only the first map has a scale bar. The working surface of all the maps is very bare, but the hedgerows and gates are shown in detailed perspective. Buildings are roughly drawn, in perspective. Laurence's own cartography is close to the style advocated by him in his 1727 book.[56] In that the engraved specimen map has a similar baroque cartouche, but the cherubs are satisfactorily youthful. There is a nicely engraved hill that looks natural, whereas Laurence's own attempt to show the relief of the land is a lumpy mess of shading. However, at that time very few estate maps made any attempt to indicate relief.

In 1727 Laurence had, with WILLIAM GARDNER, advertised[57] their joint services as land surveyors. Maybe Gardner assisted the large Maynard survey. Gardner, by himself in 1727, surveyed[58] 600 acres in Newport (near the Maynard estate) for the Earl of Thomond (The Wyndham family). Like Laurence, Gardner was not a lover of coloured maps. His Newport map has written on it: "This survey is coloured by me, Percy Wyndham".

Most probably from Northamptonshire because of his long association with the Duke of Montague of Boughton, was WILLIAM BRASIER. He was a good example of the country-bred yeoman surveyor, in contrast with Laurence, the gentleman author. Brasier surveyed widely in the home counties and was an excellent and artistic cartographer. His Essex work may well have confined to one long visit in 1730, just as much of his south Suffolk surveying was done in 1731. His career spanned from 1725 to 1757.

Illustration, page 90

His Essex work in 1730 was confined to a small area in the north of the county. There he surveyed a large farm in Elmstead[59] and the manor of Alresford[60] for Matthew Martin, a rich sea captain of the East India Company, a farm in Elmstead[61] for the Gray family of Colchester and the whole parish of Shalford[62] for the Raymond family. Another version[63] of the Shalford map dated 1734, "A curious mapp of the parish . . .", was probably made by Brasier using his 1730 survey. His maps are all attractive and informative, a balanced "whole" with good colouring. His painted cartouches have an oval "tube" entwined with flowers, a very personal creation.

Illustration, page 38

On his 1734 map is written: "Land Surveyor to His Grace the D: of Montague. This is on his Suffolk maps[64] of 1747. The connection with the Duke's family was continued for in 1752 he had on a map "Land Surveyor to the Earl of Cardigan" who was Montague's son-in-law. Two contemporaries of Brasier also claimed to be surveyors to Montague, so the appointment was not binding on one man.[65] It probably indicated a repeated commitment of a freelance surveyor who was used by many landed families of note, but not by institutions or colleges.

FROM FAR AFIELD

*I*N THIS FIRST third of the 18th century of the surveyor who made the longest journey to Essex was JOHN BURGES "of Stanton St. John, Oxon". who "Surveyed Protracted and Calculated" the 1200 acres in Childerditch owned by Edward Cheek that was once part of Lord Riches' vast estates. The map,[66] "delineated December 1701", has much florid but indifferently painted decoration, mainly around the table of contents. A crude human face, backed by sun rays is flanked by cornucopias. The table of contents is surrounded by a tendril and leaf pattern. The large divider over the scale bar has a blue ribbon with tassels entwining it. Below is a pair of terrestrial globes that do not show the continents. In all a triumph of exaggeration over proportion.

OF NO FIXED ABODE

*I*IT IS EXCEPTIONAL to find that a man who made one major survey has left no other imprint on cartographic history. DOMINIC DONNELLY is known only for his "Survey of the Lordship and Parish of Epping-berry" made in 1719 for William North.[67] The map shows 1400 acres in a somewhat clumsy layout with an over-large compass star. The wide border is a strip of printed paper pasted on, exactly like the border for Clarke's map.

The Epping estate had been surveyed[68] in 1634 by Richard Danes who also worked for Christ's Hospital and the Charterhouse. A year later the estate was bought by the North family. Donnelly's map is not a copy of Dane's work, but the product of a new survey. The sixth Baron North was imprisoned in the Tower in 1722 and then exiled to die in Madrid in 1736. His downfall was due to his Jacobite loyalties and his career was blighted by the rebellion of 1715. His Epping estate was bought by Edward Conyers in 1736. In the Conyers' archive is a terrier[69] of the estate that is a "Copy taken from Donnalak's survey, finished Dec 26, 1725, Tuesday, one o'clock". There is also an excellent undated and anonymous map[70] "copied from a plan drawn by Dominic Donnelly" that shows the Conyers' Arms instead of the Arms of the North family. As the parish of Epping was surveyed by E. J. Eyre of London in 1751 with Edward Conyers' name on the cartouche of the map[71], it is possible that Eyre made the copy of the Donnelly map.

The name Dominic Donnelly suggests an Irish Catholic. A man of that name mapped a small Dublin estate in 1703, putting after his name the initials "PM", perhaps standing for philomath. In 1760 the *Dublin Gazette* recorded the death of one of the oldest men of the time, a Dominic Donnelly who had been a professor of mathematics during the reign of Charles II.[72] Maybe this was the man who came to work for a Jacobite peer.

There is, however, another twist to the story. Shrimpton, in his thesis[73] on the 18th century landed gentry of Essex, draws attention to the first man in Essex to act as an agent to an estate. The man was Edward Browne, a carpenter in Kelvedon who, in 1717, was authorised by Abraham Barbour, a City attorney in charge of the Braxted Lodge estate, to let farms on the estate and to select tenants "which you are to do as my Baylif or agent". The collection[74] of letters to Browne, many from Barbour on estate matters, are dated from 1717 to 1721. There is one letter of 17— (the date torn off) from a D. Donnelly of London, which advises Browne on a survey of Tollesbury: ". . . go yourself to Tolsberry and gett the most intelligent of the Coppyholders to attend ye survey and show the rest of the Parish & Royalty of Tolsberry which they did not survey". The letter goes on to say that it is easy to get a list of copyholders and freeholders together with the: "computed number of acres", "as I did at Braxted in one evening". The gist of the letter strongly suggests that the writer was a surveyor. Whether the "D" stood for Dominic and whether the writer was the surveyor of Epping cannot be determined.[75]

GEORGE WASSE probably lived in or near London. His one Essex map[76] of a farm in Writtle, "survey'd September 1715" is highly coloured and rather crude in execution. The number 3 in the top corner may indicate that Wasse made other maps for William Woolf, the owner of the farm. Wasse surveyed[77] the whole manor of Sudbury in Middlesex in 1722; no other example of his work survives.

WILLIAM GODSON surveyed one of Dr Bamber's farms in Hornchurch in 1732. His survey is known from Hindley's copy[78] of his map made in 1793. The work for Bamber appears to have been at the start of Godson's career which is listed for the years 1735 to 1751. During that time he surveyed in Berkshire, Hampshire, Staffordshire and Wiltshire. No home base is known for this itinerant surveyor.

"No fixed abode" is apt for any soldier's career and certainly epitomised the life of JOHN THOMAS. His only known land surveys were for Sotheby of Waltham Holy Cross in 1723. Sotheby owned a lot of land so Thomas may have made other surveys for him, or for other clients. The Essex map[79] of a farm in Latchingdon was "An actual survey . . . by Capt. John Thomas Engin". The map is remarkable for its cartouche and for its excellent topographical representation of marsh, meadow and arable land. The buildings are shown in plan but drawn to show the pitched roofs. Trees are shown with their shadow falling to the right. The cartouche, almost a caricature of florid 17th century French maps, is in grey wash. It shows Neptune, hunched on a rock, his left arm holding a pitcher spilling water into a still pool from

Illustration page 70

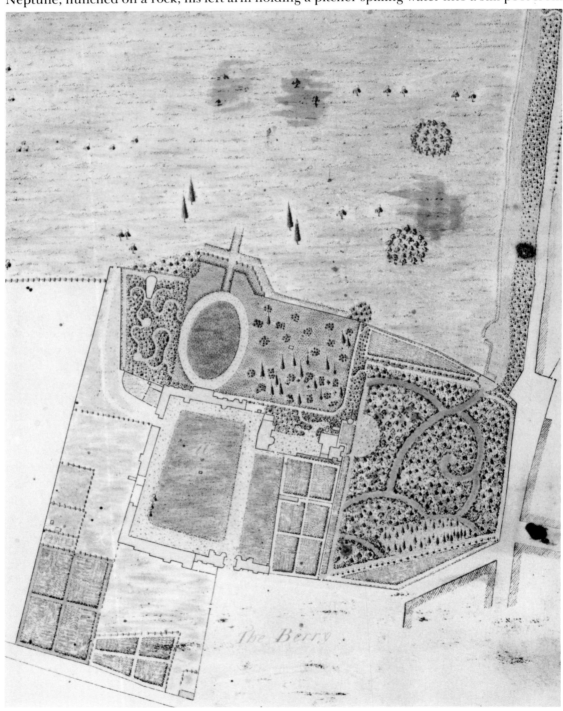

The gardens of St Osyth's Priory detailed on a map by Edward John Eyre (see p. 65), 1762. Note the parkland with copses, wilderness garden and kitchen gardens (see also illus. p. 105)

which a reptilian head emerges. His right arm is outstretched to touch the extended arm of a massive shepherdess sitting on a rock surrounded by her sheep. The other map[80] is an undecorated sketch of a small farm in Monks Eleigh, Suffolk. The scripts of both maps are poor but all is written in English. All Thomas' letters, reports and other plans are written in French for John, or Jean Thomas was a Frenchman.

Thomas' full story will be told elsewhere.[81] Briefly, he was a Huguenot who attempted to flee from France in 1686. He was arrested, condemned to the galleys, but reprieved because of his youth and schooling in mathematics and fortification. So he was sent to French Flanders as a military engineer under the great Vauban. In early 1695 he defected to the British army, bearing with him details of many of Vauban's forts in Flanders. In 1696 he was commissioned in the newly formed elite King's Company of military engineers founded by William III. However he soon fell foul of the Duke of Marlborough. Coming to England after the peace of 1697 he taught young military engineers but in 1702 served in Cadiz. He then got stuck in Ireland, planning the fortification of Londonderry in 1705. He then served in Portugal with the Earl of Galway, who, as General Massue de Ruvigny, was a fellow Huguenot. In 1716 Thomas was in Dublin desperately seeking to get back on the English pay-roll. Obviously he succeeded, as he was land surveying in Essex in 1723. As Vauban's pupil he taught fortification to the young Duke of Cumberland in 1736. Finally, in 1738 he went back on to full pay and accompanied Oglethorpe to Georgia to defend the colony against the Spaniards. There he died in 1739 but his son John, a newly commissioned military engineer, had been with him and brought back his father's plans to England. These plans of forts are well drawn with a French text and the cartouches of conventional militaria.

Essex Surveyors

NORTH ESSEX

*I*N THIS PERIOD local north Essex surveyors were mainly schoolmasters from in and around Colchester, forming a distinct group.

The Schoolmasters

At the beginning of the century JOSEPH NELSON, a teacher of mathematics, advertised[57] that he would survey land, but no work by him is known. The busy surveyors were JOHN, JOSEPH and WILLIAM KENDALL, with whom DANIEL HALLS was closely associated. HAYWARD RUSH came into the end of the period. Their known work is tabulated and shows that they worked for the landed gentry of Colchester, the Creffield, Round and Wegg families. The Round family was still employing local surveyors in the last 20 years of the century. The areas surveyed were in parishes fairly near to Colchester and few of the surveys were of more than 200 acres. The surviving maps may be only a proportion of the work that the schoolmasters did for these families.

John Storer's 1765 map is catalogued as "Surveyed by John Kendall and mapped by John Storer". However the relevant script on the map is very faded and requires close inspection under ultraviolet light before the full text becomes apparent. It reads ". . . surveyed anno 1689 by John Kendall and mapped from that survey anno 1765 by J. Storer". This early date of the survey is obviously relevant to the John Kendall maps from 1702 to 1714. On all these maps John used strong colour but usually little decoration. His 1702 map, of the largest area that he surveyed, has a cartouche including a grotesque lion mask, a decoration developed by Joseph and William. John's one survey in Suffolk was for Thomas White, an Essex man whose wood in Aldham was measured by John.

Joseph Kendall's work dates from 1703 to 1737. His written survey in Great Holland was of "land endamaged by a breach near Gunfleet Haven". He distinguished between profitable and unprofitable land. Some of the land was owned by Wheeley for whom William Kendall surveyed in Coggeshall.

TABLE THREE

WORK OF THE NORTH ESSEX SCHOOLMASTERS

Date	Name	Parish (acres)	Comment & reference
1689	John Kendall	Grt. Waltham (139)	on 1765 map by Storer D/DTu 201
1702	John Kendall	E. Mersea (61)	for Creffield D/DEt P3
1702	John Kendall	Birch (209)	for Creffield D/DEl P3
1703	Johannes Kendall	Aldham (21)	woodland D/DWe P5
1703	Jo^s Kendall	Grt. Holland (760)	written survey D/DHw E14
1710	John Kendall	*Suffolk* (Tattinghoe, 53 a.)	Copy in Suffolk R.O.
1714	Johannes Kendall	E. Mersea (75)	for Creffield D/DC 39/2
1717	(style of Kendall)	W. Mersea	T/M 445
1717	Jo^s Kendall	Copford (156)	for Round D/DR P4
1718(?)	Wm. Kendall	Colne River	Oyster lessees D/DR P6
1720	William Kendall & Daniel Halls	Coggeshall	for Wheeley Pasmore-Edwards Museum
1723	Daniel Halls	Grt. Tey (33)	D/DPb P3
1723	Daniel Halls	Hatfield Peverel (262)	D/DBd P1
1723(?)	Daniel Halls	Hatfield Peveral (217)	D/DXz 1
1724	Joseph & Wm. Kendall	White Colne (whole parish)	T/M 266
1724	Daniel Halls	Stambourne	Added to Heather's Map[5] Acc. 7920
1725	William Kendall	Birch (337)	for Round D/DR P5
1726	William Kendall	Ardleigh (125)	for Creffield D/DR P7
1730	Jo. Kendall	Grt. Clacton (96)	for Wegg D/DEl P4
1732	Joseph Kendall	Grt. Wigborough (119)	for Kilham T/M 284
1734	Hayward Rush	Wivenhoe (whole parish)	D/DU 27
1737	J. Kendall	Messing (64)	for Kilham D/DK P6
1742	Hayward Rush	Asheldham (942)	for Wegg D/DP P24
1747	Hayward Rush	Colchester	Glebe of St Mary's D/P 246

The 1724 map by Joseph and William Kendall shows the family style of decoration at its flamboyant best. Broad heavily patterned borders, lyre-shaped sides to the cartouches with a lion mask or arrogant birds, together with bright colour make all these maps instantly recognisable as Kendalls' and a pleasure to view. William went in for these elaborate decorations more than John or Joseph. The 1724 map (White Colne) was of the lands of Barwick Hall which encompassed the whole parish. There is an anonymous map of 1725 showing the land around the Hall, but this map is not in the Kendall style.

Illustration, page 55

Joseph's later work still persists with strong colour but without William's elaborations. The last Kendall map of 1737 is signed J. Kendall, but this must be Joseph as it was done for Capt. Kilham and is identical in style to the 1732 map that Joseph made for the captain.

William Kendall must have made the anonymous map of 1717 as its decoration is clearly his. Working with Daniel Halls in 1720 he let himself go by filling the lower left portion of the map with huge brilliantly coloured flowers on a single long stem. His last map is dated 1726.

Trying to place the Kendalls as a family is difficult because at that time Colchester had a plethora of Kendalls, many of them Non-conformists. However the John Kendall of the 1689 survey is almost certainly the author of *Chronometria* ("or the measurement of time"), published[82] in 1684. The book is introduced by a poem: "To my first born" by John Kendall, philomath, Colchester. The book, a detailed exposition of various aspects of astronomy, is written as a guide to astrologers. It is an important reminder that in the 17th century the term philomath often referred to astrologers. Astrology was then a respectable, and profitable, part of mathematics. John Kendall was obviously well known in the field as the foreword to his book was written by his old friend Henry Coley, surveyor and astrologer who had worked for William Lilly, who lived dangerously by making prognostications during the Civil War. Coley called Kendall a "student in the Mathematics and Coelestial Science" and much of Coley's biography in the DNB is taken from Kendall's horoscope of Coley detailed in *Chronometria*. This John Kendall bought his freedom of Colchester for £7 in 1697.[83]

The John Kendall of the 1702 to 1714 surveys is unlikely to have been the same man, if only in terms of the years passing. It is more likely to have been his son. Joseph Kendall is recorded as a schoolmaster and John Kendall as a writing master, both in Birch Magna, in the "Oath Book" of 1715.[84] This book listed those in public life who had to take an oath of allegiance after producing sacramental certificates; thus it was confined to Non-conformists. Very probably this family of Kendalls was Non-conformist. A John Kendall figures again in 1727 when, as a schoolmaster in Marks Tey, he announced[85] that he was going to open a boarding school in Kelvedon. This is likely to be the John Kendall of the 1702–14 surveys. It may not be mere coincidence that a William Kendall was a valuer and a buyer and seller of estates in Kelvedon in the 1770s.

William Kendall is known as a schoolmaster because he put "Algebraist" on his 1726 map. A speculative summary would suggest that the early John Kendall was the father of the later John and of Joseph and William.

Daniel Halls also appeared in the 1715 "Oath Book", as a schoolmaster in Halstead. On his map of 1723, made exactly in the style of William Kendall, he was "of Colchester, Philomath". His career was cut short by death, his will[86] being proved in 1730 and stating that he was a schoolmaster of Colchester. His Hatfield Peveral surveys were for William Bragge and his brother-in-law, Brabezon Aylmer, the latter survey being known from a "diminished" map by E. J. Eyre (1762). Hall's map for Bragge owes nothing to the Kendalls. Its striking feature is the hare in full flight from Conyborough field, being coursed by a pair of greyhounds watched by their two owners. But why are the greyhounds being followed by a King Charles spaniel?

Hayward Rush was, according to his maps, "Writing Master and Teacher of Navigation in Wivenhoe" in 1734 and "Land measurer and Teacher of the Mathematics in Colchester" in 1742. His 1734 map shows the whole parish of Wivenhoe and is dedicated to Isaac Rebow who bought Wivenhoe Park in that year.[87] Consequently, Halls does not show the house that

Rebow built in the park. The map has a wealth of decoration with well drawn buildings and sailing boats. Dominating the map are two panoramic views of Wivenhoe. It is of note that Rebow did not employ Halls for a survey of his Tolleshunt estates in the previous year. The Rush map of Wegg's estate in Asheldam is a colourful affair, from the cartouche and coat of arms to the compass rose. This contrasts with the 1794 anonymous map[88] of the same estate that has colour on the "working surface" but a cartouche in grey wash. The contrast is a clear illustration of how the use of colour on estate maps changed as the 18th century progressed. Rush died in Colchester in 1747, the year in which he mapped the glebe of St. Mary at the walls.

The congregation of schoolmasters in Colchester may well have had something to do with Henry Boad who was then running a school that taught navigation and land surveying.[89] There is also the thought that one of them may have taught some of the Creffield family, as there is a 1714 map[90] of 35 acres of Creffield land in Ardleigh that was made by a George Creffield. It is a plain neat map.

Surveying could well have been a useful supplement to a schoolmaster's poor stipend, but it would not make him rich. For the two special Kendall surveys, Joseph was paid £11-11-0 (1703; Grt Holland) and William received £10-15-0 for his work on the River Colne.

Other North Essex Surveyors

JEREMIAH NICHOLLS, judging from the area where he worked, probably lived in or near Bocking. His career spanned 12 years and was devoted to surveys of small parcels of land or single farms. Timber features on many of the maps, to such an extent that he might have been a carpenter or timber merchant, like the surveyor Matthew Hall of Maldon. The table sets out his known work.

TABLE FOUR

THE SURVEYS OF JEREMIAH NICHOLLS

Date	Parish (acres)	Comment & reference
1730	Braintree (14)	D/DO P1
"	Bocking (11)	D/DSv P1
"	Colne Engayne (4)	T/M 485/1
1732	Bocking (59)	D/DTa P1
"	Rivenhall (137)	D/DFg 5
1734	Felsted (58)	For R. Sayer of Braintree D/Dw P3
1735	Copford (52)	D/DEl P5
"	*Suffolk* (Bakers Hall)	D/DPa 76
1736	Finchingfield (35)	D/DU 155
1737	Belchamp Walter (187)	For Wm. Maysent D/DB P25
"	*Suffolk* (Manor of Bacons)	Suffolk R.O.
1739	Steeple Bumpstead (127)	D/DVf 4
1740?	Terling (135)	Later mapped by T. Skynner T/M 651
1741	Black Notley (woodland)	T/A 469/19
1742	Rayne (120)	For Charles Maysent D/DU 56/3

No large land owners commissioned work from Nicholls. He made two journeys to Suffolk, the first probably for an Essex client as the map is in the Papillon family archive. The Terling farm that he surveyed was bought by Strutt in 1741 and later mapped by Skynner who put no date for the map or for the survey. It is likely that Nicholls surveyed it for the previous owner. The Maysent family for whom Nicholls worked in 1737 and 1742 came from Bocking. Nicholls made simple maps with rather untidy field boundaries and without decorative features. However he used some well decorated capital letters in his titles and liked big strong Roman capitals as well. His map of Bakers Hall in Cornard, Suffolk, concentrated on the buildings as there was only a small orchard and no fields. Here Nicholls ran into trouble in laying out a quadrangle. Some of the buildings are shown "lying on their back" to show the elevation, as seen in many 16th century maps. This technique obviously fails when showing buildings forming a square. This map does show the clean lines and decorated letters of his best titles. His compass roses are multipointed stars that are rather too dominant. He put a conventional divider above a plain scale bar.

Illustration, page 125

BENJAMIN AGNIS was a Colchester farmer who did some sporadic surveying. In 1728 he mapped, for Benjamin Cock of Colchester, some land in Mayland[91] (74 a.) and Althorne[92] (30 a.). No more of his work is known until his map of a 218 a., farm in West Mersea belonging to the Charity of Arthur Winsley. This was a Colchester charity, of which the Cock family were feoffees. This map[93] was made in 1756, but the 28 year gap between maps must surely have been filled by some surveying which is unrecorded. Of course Agnis' farming must have taken up a lot of his time. But he did teach his son to survey as John Agnis mapped[94] a farm in Ardleigh in 1773.

Benjamin Agnis married Elizabeth Hendrick at St. Leonard's, Colchester in 1729. He died in 1763. His will[95] described him as "of Colchester, farmer". He left the "lease of the farm I occupy called Middlewick" to his wife Elizabeth and his son John. Small sums of money were left to his other five children.

JOHN HEATHER was a poor cartographer. For Robert Ashurst of Castle Hedingham he surveyed lands in Fairstead and Great Leighs. The surveys are dated 1720, 1721 and 1724. The maps[96] are drawn in a note book, each page containing the outline of one field. As the field numbers start at 246, he may well have made further surveys, now lost. In 1721 he surveyed in Stambourne for John Morley of Halstead. The map[97] is the only decorative one made. The title is over-written on the cartouche which is a pleasing circle of red berries and green leaves. This is in marked contrast to Heather's untidy work and suggests that some one else painted it. An addition of a parcel of land to the map in 1724 was made, not by Heather, but by Daniel Halls of Colchester. Heather's other maps, all undecorated, are of a farm (1722) in Sible Hedingham[98] owned by a charity of that parish, of a bigger farm[99] away in Steeple (1724) but owned by a man of Belchamp Otten, and a parcel of land in Great Maplestead[100] (1725). The location of the lands surveyed and of their owners suggests that Heather lived in or near Castle Hedingham. He probably surveyed by the chain only as on all his maps is written "Measured by Mr Gunter's four pole chain". His polar indicators all have an apology for a fleur de lys, drawn as a triangle with two rough crescents below.

THOMAS HOLMES made "An Exact and Perfect Survey"[101] of the whole parish of Quendon in 1702, depicting the same land as shown on a map[102] of 1645. This map pictured some men and animals in the fields. Holmes went one better, populating his fields with three horsemen with a pack of hounds, a man shouldering a gun, and some deer. On this map, as on his map (1706) of 318 acres in Thaxted[103] he painted a fine achievement of the owner's arms. His other map[104] (1700) shows a 439 acre farm in Paglesham, well away from his usual area of survey. This map has a large compass star, the centre formed by a globe inscribed with the signs of the zodiac. All his known surveys are of large areas and all his maps show considerable artistic imagination. His scant surviving work indicates that he was a surveyor of merit employed by people with quite large estates. Yet nothing else is known of him.

Illustrations, pages 59, 133

This account of surveyors working in north Essex must include the major surveys of Coggeshall in 1731–3 by Timothy Skynner. The career of this man is fully described under the second time period when he was flourishing. Sufficient at this point is the query as to whether there were two Skynners, father and son. Evidence to show that this is likely will be presented.

At this period of the 18th century North Essex had an interesting "mix" of land surveyors. Notable is the absence of Suffolk men. The Creffield family, Sir Isaac Rebow and others, relied on the local schoolmasters, while Mathew Martin and the Raymond family brought in a full-time yeoman surveyor, William Brasier. Lord Maynard, with by far the largest estate, employed the gentleman, author and expert on estate management, Edward Laurence. Later Maynard resorted to an Essex man, Timothy Skynner.

CENTRAL ESSEX

THE DANBURY-MALDON area produced two local land surveyors of considerable merit. BENJAMIN FALLOWES had a brief, exceptionally busy career from 1714 to 1720. The scale of his work rivalled that of the "outsiders" like Laurence or Brasier in North Essex. He was the only local Essex man throughout the century to make a long journey for a commission.

It is not certain that he was born an Essex man but, from his maps, he lived in Danbury in 1714 and was in Maldon by early 1715. There he stayed until 1720. At some time after that he moved to Purleigh where he was farming in 1726. The lack of his record in parish registers can be put down to the fact that he was a Quaker. The book[105] of the monthly meetings of "The People of God, called in scorn Quakers" (the Witham meetings) states that in March 1720 there came to a meeting at Chelmsford "Benjamin ffallowes of Maldon, widower, and Elizabeth Tallen of Heybridge, widow, and declared their intention of marriage". In this context it is of note that Fallowes in 1716 surveyed the Feering estate of John Raven, one of the best known of Essex Quakers. The second marriage heralded the end of Fallowes' career as a surveyor, his last map[106] dated 28 November 1726 depicting the farm he occupied in Purleigh. Farming these 316 acres must have been a sufficient occupation. Here was a full-time surveyor turned farmer, in contrast to several Essex farmers who surveyed as well. Fallowes did not farm for long as he must have died before April 1731 when the Purleigh parish register recorded the burial of "Ann Fallows, daughter of Benjamin, deceased".

Fallowes habitually dated each map by year, month and day. The list of his maps for 1716 indicates that the dating must represent the completion of a map and that several surveys and maps were in process at any one time. So much work was completed in 1716 that most of the previous year must have been taken up with these surveys. The dating gives no clue as to how long he may have taken on a survey. His distinctive cartographic style is already well developed in his first surviving map[107] of 1714. This "true draught" of 117 acres in Dengie was made for R. Mead of "Greenwitch". London gentlemen feature as clients for other surveys; for W. Swan in Maldon[108] (1717), for H. Olmius Jnr.[109] in Felstead (1717) and Great Leighs[106] (1720) and for Thomas Inwen in Purleigh[110] (1726) whose farm was occupied by Fallowes. The major feature of the Fallowes style was the use of individual flowers to border a map, or a floral design to a border. His compass roses are beautifully realised and the well drawn divider above a simple scale bar have a distinctive curve in each limb. The cartouches are usually simple but sometimes he used well coloured "moulding" to frame the title. On occasion he conjured up some exotic birds as decoration. A map by Fallowes is instantly recognisable by his personal decorative style that did not alter through his short career. The

Illustration, page 98

anonymous map[111] of Wickford, although undecorated, can be attributed to Fallowes by its script and layout, apart from documentary evidence to suggest that he was the cartographer.

The great bulk of Fallowes' work was carried out for the Western family. In 1716 he went up to Cambridgeshire to survey[112] Abington Hall, the property of Maximillan Western of London. At the end of that year he made two surveys for Robert Western. The first, of 172 acres in Braintree, is known only from a written account.[113] This lists the parcels "comprised in an exact map . . . by Benj. Fallowes of Maldon, Surveyor". The remarks in this document are of interest. Of the acreage listed "The total is different from that stated on the map which appears to be occasioned by a clerical error". The document, prepared for a particular of sale, refers to a new map, made after the Fallowes' survey. "The outward boundary of the whole estate is exactly the same in the old map as in the new, tho' the divisions of the fields is somewhat different, but may easily be ascertained by inspection of the maps". Here is a clear indication of the "bread and butter" work of a local surveyor, checking alterations in a property prior to its sale. The other Robert Western property was in Wickford and the subject of the anonymous map already mentioned. The two surveys are dated the 7th and 15th of December respectively.

TABLE FIVE

THE MAPS OF BENJAMIN FALLOWES DATED 1716

Month	Day	Parish	Acres	Comment
Feb.	7	*Cambridgeshire*	636	For Max. Western
Mar.	31	Althorn	355	For Will. Western
April	9	Feering	111	For John Raven
"	9	Creeksea	305	For Will. Western
"	10	" "	385	" "
May	21	Rivenhall	240	" "
"	25	" "	193	" "
"	31	" "	193	" "
June	4	" "	221	" "
"	7	" "	327	" "
"	9	" "	120	" "
"	13	" "	176	" "
"	26	" "	95	" "
"	28	Witham	234	" "
July	21	Denge	174	" "
"	21	Rivenhall	153	" "
Aug.	9	Mundon	113	" "
"	14	Rivenhall	245	" "
"	18	Rettenden	225	" "
"	23	" "	202	" "
Sept.	19	Mundon	113	" "
"	22	" "	318	" "
Oct.	17	Purleigh	73 (wood)	" "
"	22	" "	104 (wood)	" "
Dec.	7	Stambridge	412	" "
"	7	Braintree	179	For Robert Western
"	15	Wickford	199	" "

The great bulk of Fallowes' work was for "my most worthy Master William Western . . . humbly presented . . . by Benjamin Fallowes of Maldon". The term "master" may have implied that Fallowes was his servant or that William Western was young. He inherited these Rivenhall Place estates from his grandfather in 1712. Old Thomas Western, citizen and grocer of London, outlived his son and died in 1706. It took six years, an Act of

Parliament and a committee of 10 bishops and 20 lords before William, a minor, could possess the estates. A field book of some of the estate made by Fallowes describes the lands as belonging to Thomas Western.

The Western estates were mainly in Rivenhall but there were also considerable holdings in Mundon, Rettenden and Purleigh. The first maps of the series are dated March 1715 (Latchingdon, 550 a, and Mundon Hall, 795 acres) and the rest are all dated 1716. The last of the 26 maps in the series is dated 6 June 1717 and shows the whole of Runsel Hamlet, Danbury. These maps,[14] bound into a large volume, are full of information and of considerable artistic merit. They show Fallowes as a top rank surveyor of his time.

The year 1718 marked Fallowes' long journey to the west. In June, July and August of that year he produced a series of maps[115] covering the Earl of Abergavenny's estates in Monmouth, Hereford and Worcestershire. Presumably the earlier months had been taken up for the actual survey work. There are no Essex surveys for that year. As for Western, Fallowes had his series of maps bound into one volume and their decoration is exactly as on the Western maps. Twelve maps are included. In 1805 David Davies, a local Welsh surveyor, made reduced copies[116] of "The Earl of Abergavenny's Large Book of Maps . . . by Benjamin Fallowes". When the estate was resurveyed in 1821 it was Davies who did it. Certainly Fallowes' survey proved its value by long use, but there is no explanation as to why he was preferred over any London or Welsh surveyor to do the job in the first place.

Fallowes' work for London gentlemen has already been noted. The only well known Essex man for whom he worked, other than the Western family, was Sir Robert Abdy of Stapleford Abbotts. His farm in Great Wigborough was mapped[117] in 1719 and the cartouche includes two grotesque human faces intertwined with flowers, an unusually complicated scene for Fallowes. The bigger estate in Tolleshunt Knights was surveyed[118] in 1720. All these surveys were of areas of around 200–400 acres, and Fallowes left no work on small parcels of land that form much of the work by many Essex surveyors.

An interesting spin-off from Fallowes' work for William Western is a series of four maps[119] entitled: "Taken from an original survey and map made in the year 1716 by Wm Appleby Snr. . . . and now in the possession of Charles Western, 1803". The title is ambiguous. It could mean that the copies were taken from a survey by Appleby, or that Appleby took a copy of the 1716 survey by Fallowes. The maps are not copies of the Fallowes maps. Two of the farms shown were in the occupation of William Appleby when Fallowes made his survey. It seems likely that Appleby had enough cartographic skill to produce maps of his own and his neighbours' farms, using the 1716 survey of Fallowes. It would be odd if he actually made his own survey of these farms in the same year that they were surveyed by Fallowes. Appleby's entry in the Dictionary of Surveyors is not really merited on the dubious evidence that he was a surveyor.

JOHN LEE was close to Fallowes in time, place and a love of floral decoration for his earlier maps. His surveying career was long, from 1718 to 1756, and he flourished into a ripe old age as his last entry in his commonplace book was made in 1773. Extracts from this book and a brief biography of Lee were recorded[120] by J. Berridge. According to him, Lee was the son of a farmer and born at Boreham in 1693. In his youth, Lee lived in Little Baddow and then in Danbury (where Fallowes lived in 1714). Most of his adult life was spent in Great Baddow where the Poll Book of 1763 shows him to have possessed sufficient estate for him to qualify as an elector.

All Lee's surveys were of areas close to Great Baddow, although his commonplace book indicates that he travelled widely in southern England for pleasure. On his maps he was fond of using the formula: "An exact draught . . . by me, John Lee". All his surveys (with three exceptions, including a 45 a. farm in Ingatestone,[121] 1719) were of well over 100 acres and the land owners were the local landed gentry, rather than the land-rich aristocrats.

In December 1718, the year that Fallowes went to Wales, Lee produced his first map,[122] of a farm in East Hanningfield belonging to the Bonnell family of Danbury. His first major work was the survey of the whole parish of Sandon in 1721 for Anthony Collins who owned the two manors concerned. This huge map[123] (43″ by 61″) has an anachronistic cartouche of Elizabethan strap-work, but it is enlivened with some flowers. The borders and the scale bar are decorated and, as on his other maps, the polar indicator is a complex multistar pattern. About this time he must have surveyed Mr Hoare's New Hall at Boreham, work recorded in Lee's commonplace book. Hoare bought the property in 1713 and sold it in 1728. Later (1753) Lee surveyed[124] two large farms in Bradwell belonging to Benjamin Hoare.

Monochrome cartouche by James Bermingham (see p. 67), 1738. The mantle motif recurs, in differing styles, throughout the century. For a crude example, see p. 79.

In 1724 Lee was surveying[125] the foreshore of Prittlewell for the Scrutton family when he was interrupted by the oyster snatchers from Kent. The Scrutton family archive contains two further maps of land and sea ground in Prittlewell. The maps,[126] dated 1749 and 1750 are anonymous and undecorated. It is possible that they are of further surveys by Lee.

Also in 1724 there is a written "measure"[127] of woods in Woodham Ferris belonging to the Strutt family. This is headed: ". . . by John Lee of Great Baddow", something that he never wrote on his maps. The Strutt connection was repeated by Lee's survey[128] of a farm in Woodham Ferrers in 1756. The map is by Skynner who clearly stated: "Surveyed by John Lee 1756". This was the last work of Lee's, and once more shows long ties with families who may well have employed him for other work that is not recorded.

The most decorative map[129] and the most extensive survey by Lee was carried out in 1725 for the Governors of Chelmsford Grammar school. The map shows properties in several parishes, from Tilbury to Hatfield Peverel. The decoration shows Lee at his bright coloured best. The title is flanked by a pair of red and gold cornucopias issuing flowers on which butterflies and insects are settling. There is also a spray of gilliflowers. Whereas Fallowes used larger bold flowers, and the occasional exotic bird, Lee worked on a smaller more delicate style to produce the same effect. He used the same type of decoration on his map[130] of a farm in Birdbrook (1726) and of a larger farm,[131] belonging to Jacob Houblon, then acquiring a large estate, in Aythorpe Roding (1728). The 1726 map had an unusual compass rose that incorporated a globe showing the continents. The borders of these maps were decorated with a leaf and flower pattern. A slight variation is the wide quatrefoil leaf pattern for the border and the lightly moulded baroque cartouche with a huge rose springing from either side shown on Lee's map[132] of a farm in Cressing belonging to John Wright (1727).

Illustration pages 63, 99

Lee's sketch map[133] of Mangap farm in Burnham, a Mildmay property, was made in 1728 but, curiously, was neglected when the farm was surveyed by Hutson of Hutton in 1777. Hutson made a formal map and a preliminary plan on which he noted field alterations compared with a map of 1651. But in 1745 Lee surveyed[134] a small farm in Hockley for the Mildmays.

A rough undecorated map[135] of Stanford bridge made by Lee in 1729 is of interest as it illustrates, not only the bridge itself, but also what part of the bridge had to be kept up by the contiguous parishes of Stanford, Mucking and Horndon. The original map is in the Public Record Office, part of a miscellaneous collection of documents collected by 18th century Deputy Chamberlains of the Exchequer. The map is probably associated with John Lawton who succeeded Peter le Neve, the antiquarian, as Deputy Chamberlain in 1712. Associated documents in this collection indicate that Lawton was building a house in Stanford le Hope in 1726. His connection with the upkeep of the bridge is not revealed.

The later work of Lee that has not been mentioned consists of a survey of a farm[136] in Writtle (1735) for George Bramston and of the 435 a. manor of Gobions in Mucking[137] (1738). One of his last works was of Great Baddow[138] in 1754: "The Bounds according to the Ancient and Customary Perambulation thereof survey'd 1732". The map follows a similar boundary map drawn by William Cole in 1708.

Lee's long life after he gave up surveying was presumably supported from his land, as a farmer like his father.

Associated with John Lee was WILLIAM PULLEN, Philomath of Chelmsford as he declared on his first map[139] (1731) showing a 110 a., farm in Ingatestone. The map contains a neat picture of the SE prospect of Hyde House. In 1734 he surveyed[140] for the Strutt family a farm in Terling called Great Hooks, "vulgarly called Porridge-Pot Hall". This was later remapped by Skynner from Pullen's survey. The Lee/Strutt connection is underlined by a sheet of paper[141] attached to Lee's written wood survey of 1724 for Strutt. The paper records that: "Mr Studford's wood is seven acres and 30 poles, measured on 24 May 1737 by W. Pullen". Pullen's other known map[142] shows a 125 a. farm in Springfield (1735). This lists all the trees by species and number. There is minimal decoration compared with his 1734 map which is bordered by pendant fuchsia flowers that flow along the base and a scroll cartouche decorated with fuchsia leaves.

As a philomath Pullen was probably a Chelmsford schoolmaster who only surveyed for this short six year period. It is possible that he was related to the John Pullen, "Teacher of the Mathematics" in Temple Bar (1719) who surveyed in Sussex.[65]

The map[143] of Isaac Rebow's estates in Tolleshunt D'arcy was "Taken by me" JEREMIAH LOAN in 1728. This is the only known work by Loan. The map is well drawn; the cartouche, in broad strokes of colour, suggests a globe of the world. The Red Lion inn is neatly drawn to show the inn sign hanging out. Rebow used Rush of Wivenhoe in 1734 to survey his estate there.

EDWARD SOLME "carefully surveyed" and mapped[144] a 110 a. farm in Tolleshunt D'arcy in 1709. Perhaps he was the Edward Solme, Gent., of Springfield, Chelmsford, listed in the Oath Book of 1714–6. The same name appears on John Lee's 1721 map of Sandon as a holder of small parcels of land. No other surveys by Solme are known but his one map is clear and neatly drawn without decoration.

JOHN FOSTER made two maps in 1712 for Mr Robert Clarks, one "a figure of . . ." a farm in Wix[145] (82 a.) and the other "a little farm"[146] of 27 a. in Wrabness. He quoted the total acreage on the Wix map, explaining: " . . . as may be seen from the contents of each piece being put in the part of each piece", a glimpse of the obvious that no experienced surveyor used.

In the west of central Essex two names briefly appear. In 1700 MICHAEL MARTIN mapped just 12 acres in Roydon.[147] For this insignificant parcel he created most elaborate and artistic decoration. Like Lee, he used two cornucopias from which flowed a large naturalistic leaf and flower pattern that encloses the whole map with bright colour. The embellishments suited the title: "This mapp as a monument of gratitude is humbly offered and presented by Michael Martin Practitioner in Arts Mathematical" to Richard Childs of Wanstead Place. Richard Childs had taken over his half-brother's estates the year before Martin's small survey. Was the gratitude for favours received, or a means of obtaining them? As practitioner of arts mathematical Martin can be said to have been a schoolmaster but the title could also imply a practice in astrology, like John Kendall of Colchester.

MICHAEL SHERWOOD surveyed only in 1730 and 1731. For Richard Luther of Kelvedon Hatch he surveyed "three farms lying together" in White Roothing[148] (1730) and two in Roxwell[149] (1731). For Thomas Worford he surveyed two farms lying in High

Roothing and High Easter. His cartouches are of routine classical type done in sepia. The scripts of the titles are highly decorated. An extremely unusual point on his White Roothing map is "Magnetic meridian anno 1730" written alongside the polar indicator. Sherwood's short career in surveying, elegant scripts and comment on the magnetic pole suggest that he may have been a schoolmaster, possibly living in Kelvedon Hatch. He does not figure in the list of that parish's rate payers, but to do so would mean the possession of property.

SOUTH ESSEX

*I*N THE FIRST third of the century the western parishes of south Essex, near to London, do not appear to have been the subject of any major survey. Some local surveyors do have a record.

JOHN MORGAN surveyed[151] a house and its grounds in West Ham on "Oct. ye 5, 1725", probably for a change of tenancy as the map is endorsed: "Now leased to . . . Oct 28, 1725".

THOMAS ARCHER who worked in Leyton and Walthamstow, is likely to have been the Leyton freeholder of that name who was 40 years old in 1734. His first survey,[152] dated 1721, was of the Leyton manor of Ruckholds, bought the year before by Collier. The manor was resurveyed in 1728 by Cushee of London when it had been bought by the Childs family. Archer's 1725 survey[153] of 36 acres in Walthamstow was ". . . measured the 30th day of September", suggesting the work of one day and in accord with Dr Eden's opinion that around 20 acres a day was the average stint of a land measurer. Also in Walthamstow, Archer produced in 1726, an entrancing plan[154] rather than map to show "Forest Hall Built A.D. 1726" and other buildings. The upper half of the map shows the elevation of the buildings, painted realistically in great detail. In the sky above the houses are two cherubs holding a banner on which the title is written. The bottom half of the "map" shows the buildings in ground plan with the surrounding land. There is a scale bar but without any unit of measurement.

The only other known work of Archer's is a 1728 copy[155] copy of a Norfolk estate map made in 1660.

In 1723 ADAM HOLT surveyed[156] the manor of Aldersbrooke, Wanstead, surveyed again in 1748 by John Noble of London. Holt was first known to the Rector of Wanstead in 1729, was listed in 1734 as a 43 year old freeholder of that Parish, to which he was an overseer of the poor in 1735.[157] Nothing more is known of Holt's surveying until in 1743 he surveyed a large scattered estate, based on Epping, of a London merchant's widow. His map[158] displays the lands in nine neat "boxes" with an improved script.

Like Holt, JAMES CRADOCK was a Wanstead rate payer (in 1735). He worked only for the Child's family of Wanstead Place, which he mapped[159] (undated). In 1725 he made five maps[160] of the family's farms in Felsted. He may well have surveyed more, for the numbers on the back of the maps do not run consecutively and the area mapped is but a portion of the whole Felsted estate as surveyed by Mumford and Doyley in 1796.

Cradock's cartography was unusual and retrogressive. The "working surface" of his maps was painted, not drawn. So the boundary hedgerows are a pastiche of colour rather than the accurate line needed to show land divisions. However he used elegant scripts with "swash" capitals and looped line decoration instead of a cartouche, the style of a 17th century writing master.

WILLIAM STANE of Romford was a major 17th century surveyor. The early 18th century saw the dwindling of his long career with three maps of small areas in Romford[161] (1706) and

Stapleford Abbots (1706?[162] and 1718).[163] The 1718 map is really a draft signed by Stane in the manner he used for documents relating to his estate. The three maps are in the Mildmay archive.

Stane flourished from 1669 and made several major surveys, notably his 1691 maps[164] of William Petre's manor of South Ockenden and of Kirby Hall, Castle Hedingham.[165] His cartography gave a clear outline of the land. He used highly decorated scripts for his titles without a cartouche. His only other decoration was a very large well drawn pair of dividers over a simple scale bar. Stane's work must be related to that of his successful colleague and contemporary, John Coffyn of Great Burstead. Both men were Roman Catholics and both surveyed for the Petre family, the premier Catholic family in the district.[166] Stane was a gentleman with a fair estate in Romford that he inherited from an uncle in Oxfordshire in 1667. When Stane died in 1723 he made several bequests to charity, including the Romford Charity School.[167]

Contents table from a map of Chigwell Grange, by George Sangster (see p. 86), 1769. The contents table was a practical device for containing information on an otherwise often crowded map while providing an at-a-glance summary of the owner's property (see also illus. p. 95)

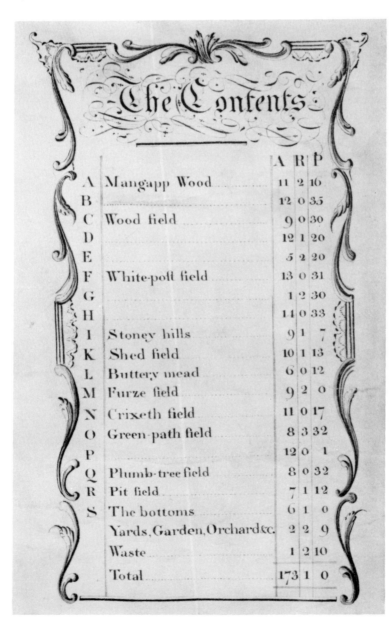

		A	R	P
A	Mangapp Wood	11	2	16
B		12	0	35
C	Wood field	9	0	30
D		12	1	20
E		5	2	20
F	White-poll field	13	0	31
G		1	2	30
H		14	0	33
I	Stoney hills	9	1	7
K	Shed field	10	1	13
L	Buttery mead	6	0	12
M	Furze field	9	2	0
N	Crixeth field	11	0	17
O	Green-path field	8	3	32
P		12	0	1
Q	Plumb-tree field	8	0	32
R	Pit field	7	1	12
S	The bottoms	6	1	0
	Yards, Garden, Orchard &c.	2	2	9
	Waste	1	2	10
	Total	173	1	0

JOHN COFFYN of Great Burstead was undoubtedly the major Essex land surveyor of the late 17th century. Apart from his Essex work for Bramston of Skreens and for Lord Petre, he surveyed in Kent, Surrey and Leicestershire. His very distinctive style of decoration was modelled on the "continuous line" patterns beloved by 17th century writing masters.

Coffyn's personal contribution to the 18th century was a map[168] (1701) of a 40 acre messuage in Buttsbury, but he had considerable influence through the work of William Cole and, later, Robert Parker. Coffyn's own estate was small, but his spinster daughter Mary inherited from her godmother, one of the Audley family, the manor of Broxted. Her neat signature as Lord of the Manor is on the Court Baron record of 1700. She also held property in Ramsden Belhus.

WILLIAM COLE, yeoman of Ramsden Belhus, made his first map in 1700. This was a busy year for him. He married Elizabeth Watts of the same parish and in the company of Robert Watts was assaulted and robbed. That he was probably a pupil of John Coffyn's is evident from the style of his cartography. Moreover, Mary Coffyn appointed him as her official "friend" when her estate was registered as belonging to a Roman Catholic, and Cole surveyed[169] her

Cartouche and decorative border by William Kendall (see p. 45), 1726. Kendall's brightly coloured "primitive' style contrasts with the subtler sophistication of Brasier's cartouche of similar date (p. 38). Decorative borders were out of fashion by the 1730s.

manor of Broxted. Cole himself may well have been a Catholic, although there is no proof of this. Certainly he did much work for Lord Petre.

Illustrations pages 27, 129

Cole followed Coffyn's style so closely that an anonymous map[170] of 1687 has been wrongly attributed to him rather than Coffyn. However the map shows one part of a larger survey displayed in a map[171] of that date signed by Coffyn. Cole used Coffyn's continuous line decoration for his cartouches and scale bars, but used colour to fill several of his looped ink-lines. In his early maps he put the points of the compass in the four borders of the map and omitted a polar indicator. His scripts are very similar to those used by Coffyn, but more spiky and less elegant. Cole, like Coffyn, surveyed mainly in south-east Thames-side Essex. He added to Coffyn's 1687 map[171] of Shoebury, and he went north to Broxted to survey Mary Coffyn's manor.

Cole had a trade in the measurement of small scattered woods, showing them in crude plain maps, indicating acreage and shape. For Sir Francis St. John he made such surveys in Leigh and nearby in 1709, 1710, 1713, 1714 and 1716 (the original maps are in the Huntingdon-shire Record Office). He did the same for Lord Petre, measuring woods in Ingrave[172] and nearby in 1700, 1706, 1710, 1725 and 1727. These woodland surveys are not listed on the table of his land surveys. The table shows that he usually surveyed a large area such as a manor, and did little work on small parcels of land. Apart from going to Broxted, his only other journey north was to Grange Manor, Coggeshall.

New College, Oxford, did not employ Cole for its 1717 survey of Hornchurch, land previously surveyed by Coffyn; a London surveyor was used. Kings College, Cambridge, employed Cole and Parker to survey its land in Benfleet (1722). The map was sent by the tenant to the College in 1748 but was missing from the College archive in 1879. A few years ago it reached the Essex Record Office from a Southend solicitor.

Cole had a long association with Lord Petre, not only for his woods but also, with Parker, in

TABLE SIX

THE SURVEYS OF WILLIAM COLE

Date	*Parish*	*Comment*	*Reference*
1700	Canvey	Marsh land	D/DU 33/1
"	Wakering	Marsh land	T/M 9
1706	Ramsden Crays	15 a. Messuage	D/DB P53
1708	Baddow	Part of parish bounds	D/DK P3
"	S. Shoebury	Add. to Coffyn's map	in Southend Museum
1709	Coggeshall	Grange manor, 392 a.	D/DU 1497/1.
1711	Asheldham	Marsh land, 417 a.	D/DP P17
"	Woodham Ferrers	Champions manor, 664 a.	D/DRa P2
1713	Broxted	Mary Coffyn's manor	D/DBe P8
1714	Bradwell	Manor, 434 a.	T/M 301
1716	Lt. Stambridge	Manor	D/DU 190/23
"	Lambourne	2 small farms (for Lockwood)	D/DU 354
1717	Prittlewell	Manor + woods (for Bristow)	D/DNe P10 & D/DS 9/2
1719	N. Shoebury	Farm, 170 a.	D/DQh 2
"	Childerditch	Farm, 18 a. (Lady Tipping)	D/DP P77
1720	" " "	Common, 382 a. (Lady Tipping)	D/DP P77
"	Mayland	Farm, map by Dayles, 1739	D/DP P105
"	Canewdon	Scots Hall manor, 382 a.	D/DB P3
1722	S. Benfleet	With Parker. Marsh land	D/DGs P7
1723	N. Shoebury	47 a. of manor land	D/DU 663/3
"	Thundersley	Farm 230 a.	D/DFa P3
1724	Writtle	With Parker. Ld Petre's farm, 334 a.	D/DP P20

surveying a large farm in Writtle. His map of the bounds of Great Baddow (mapped again by Lee in 1754) was "according to the description of some Ancient Men . . .", indicating the importance of local knowledge to a land surveyor.

ROBERT PARKER of Runwell was the son of Charles Parker, a Roman Catholic yeoman whose estate was larger than Coffyn's. Robert must have been occupied farming some of this land, but he had a tenant for one farm (he also owned a messuage called the Quart Pot). Parker was closely associated with Cole and with Lord Petre. For Petre, Parker and Cole were co-surveyors in 1722 and 1724. Parker alone surveyed Petre's 440 acre farm in Roxwell[173] in 1728 and the glebe of Little Burstead[174] in 1731. His cartography closely followed Cole's style, and thus was like Coffyn's. However he used more colour in his decoration and a broader pen.[175]

Outside the Petre estates, Parker made one map for St Bartholomew's Hospital. His little draught map[176] of woodland near Runwell was pasted on the Treswell 1587 map of the whole hospital estate in Downham and Ramsden Belhus. This was done in 1746, the year when the Hospital's Governors decreed new surveys for estates not previously mapped fully. John Noble was commissioned to carry this out. He was not asked to come from London to check the wood near Runwell. It looks as if the minor day to day surveying work on an estate already mapped was left to a local man. If so, then Parker may well have had a long term watching brief on the nearby Hospital estates.

The last two maps in Lord Petre's book of wood surveys (mainly by Cole) are by PHILLIP WHITTINGTON. The maps, dated 1732, are the only evidence of his work as a surveyor. According to the list[177] of Lord Petre's full-time employees at Thorndon Park (1742) Whittington was a bailiff. As such he appears in the rent books, collecting the quit rents for the manors of Mountnessing, Bacons and Buttsbury. He must have been well acquainted with the little coterie of Catholic land surveyors employed by Petre and all living close together.

High on the list of Petre's servants was "Mr Bourginion, Surveyor". In fact, Bourginion was a French designer of gardens, nicknamed by the Petres "the constable". A beautiful design[178] for the gardens of Thorndon Park is endorsed: "designed by the Sieur. Bourginion". "I hope the Lord will not outrun the Constable in his designs at Thorndon" was a family comment on Lord Petre's enthusiasm. A similar scheme,[179] in the same baroque fashion was made for Weald Hall. The plan is anonymous but has been attributed to Bourginion. However the style is French, rather than personal. Exactly the same style was used by John Rocque for Wanstead Place[180] (1735), and on the plan of the gardens of Audley End[181] (circa 1725), almost certainly made by Charles Bridgeman and the French military engineer turned architect, Charles Dubois.

After this diversion into garden designers and their plans, there is one more name for a surveyor living somewhere around Ramsden Belhus. WESTON WEALD was the surveyor of woods "taken off ye commons in the parish of Ramsden Bellows". The map,[182] dated 1732 is the only known work of this man. The name Weald or Weld was fairly common in that part of Essex.

Further to the east, Great Stambridge Hall, owned by the Charterhouse, was mapped[183] in 1722 and 1725 by the same hand whose name is encoded in a monogram that defies analysis. But the 18th century catalogue of Charterhouse maps names him as J. ROBART.

This monogram is unique among Essex estate maps. Robart was not skilled as his colours were poorly mixed. This serves as a reminder that cartographers had to prepare their own pigments, suspend them in a gum arabic solution and then colour the map already drawn in ink and with the surface coated with alum water to prevent the colour soaking through. Text books of surveying gave detailed instructions on the preparation and application of colours; a time-consuming skill.

References and Notes (Part II First Period)

1 D/DXb 48.
2 Details taken from T. Campbell, 1973, "The Drapers Company and its school of 17th century chart-makers" in *My Head is a Map* Eds H. Wallis and S. Tyacke. London. F. Edwards & Carter Press.
3 The maps are in the Hertfordshire Record Office.
4 The maps were engraved on seven sheets by I. Harris. Copies in Map Library, British Library.
5 D/DU 64.
6 D/DB P32.
7 D/DNe P2.
8 Map in Guildhall Library.
9 D/DWe P4.
10 Facts provided by the College of Arms. Browne's date of birth confirmed by his statement that he was 47 years old in 1749. DNB gives his year of birth as 1706. Sir Anthony Wagner, in his *Heralds of England* (1967; HMSO), quotes from an 18th century manuscript in the College of Arms that is highly critical of Browne for not being born a gentleman and knowing little about heraldry. Browne, it says, was "a poor ragged boy of very mean parentage, a servant to Warburton Somerset Herald whom he employ'd to . . . hawk his maps of Middlesex and allowed him a small sum for each he sold". "By attendance on his master in surveying lands" Browne "got some little knowledge". The biography claims that Browne married for money and got to know his rich patrons by becoming a

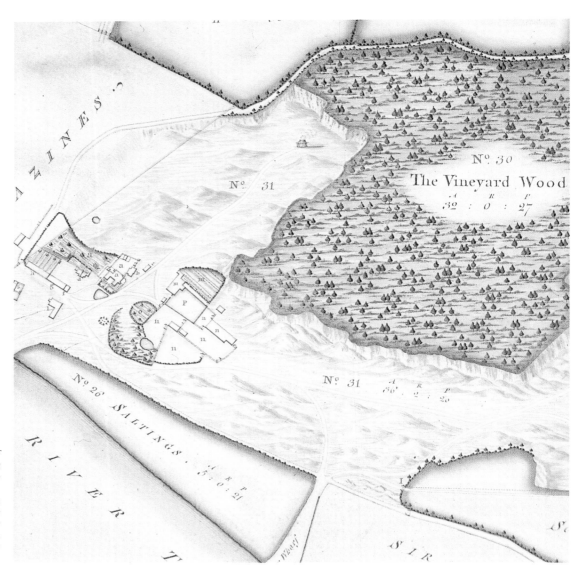

Detail from a map of Purfleet Farm, West Thurrock by Thomas Bateman (see p.69), 1767 showing chalk quaries beside the Thames. Note the combination of strict plan and topographical "birds eye view" drawing.

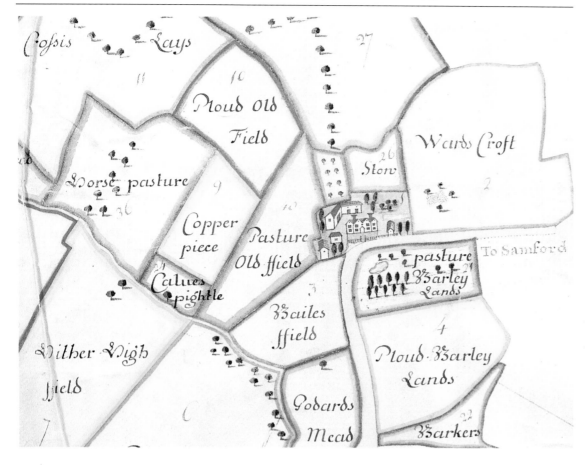

Goddard's Farm, Thaxted with surrounding fields, by Thomas Holmes (see p. 47), 1706. The crude elevation of buildings, looking back to the 17th century, were frowned on by the more sophisticated mapmakers of the next century, unless used for specific effect (see the lime-kiln on Bateman's map, opposite).

herald just in time to join the coronation procession of George II. Browne, it states, became a "considerable land broker" and "as such was admitted to the intimacy of the first Men of this Time".

11 D/DZn 3.
12 Map in Map Library, British Library.
13 D/DU 431.
14 Map and documents in Public Record Office.
15 D/DBe E8.
16 D/DBe E10.
17 D/DBe P2, 3.
18 D/DBe P4.
19 D/DBe P5.
20 D/DBe E6.
21 Maps in Hertfordshire Record Office.
22 Map in Guildhall Library.
23 Map in New College, Oxford (ERO photograph T/M 154).
24 See E. G. R. Taylor; 1966. *The Mathematical Practitioners of Hanoverian England*. Cambridge.
25 D/DCy P3A.
26 D/DU 245.
27 D/SH 14.
28 D/DSt P1.
29 See Munk's Roll, Royal College of Physicians of London.
30 D/DBi P1.
31 Map in private hands.
32 D/DQy 2.
33 Kingsman's two maps, timber survey and bills are in the Library, the Royal College of Physicians of London.
34 F. Hull, 1987. From *An Essex Tribute*. Ed. K. Neale. Leopards Head Press.

35 D/DQs 28.
36 Map in Cambridge University Library.
37 D/DS 120.
38 Maps in Gonville & Caius College, Cambridge. (Photographs in ERO.)
39 Facts kindly supplied by Miss A. Oakley, archivist to Canterbury Cathedral.
40 D/Q 18 P2.
41 D/DU 47.
42 D/DR P8.
43 The hospital's archives are in the GLC Record Office.
44 D/DU 19/1.
45 D/DU 19/4. Gould "viewed" a Surrey farm of Du Cane's in 1718.
46 Archives of the Corporation in GLC Record Office. Some of the Corporation's maps are in Cambridge University Library.
47 D/DQ 88/2.
48 D/DEt P6.
49 D/DQ 88/3.
50 D/DWv P3.
51 Maps in Suffolk Record Office.
52 From Laurence's *Young Surveyor's Guide;* 1726.
53 The bill for this survey was found by Dr Peter Eden.
54 D/DU 583/2.
55 D/DMg P1.
56 E. Laurence; 1727. *The Duty of a Steward to his Lord.*
57 From E. G. R. Taylor Op. cit.
58 T/M 298.
59 D/DC 39/3.
60 Map in private hands.
61 D/DRb P1.
62 T/M 472.
63 D/DSm P3.
64 Maps in Suffolk Record Office.
65 Details from *Dictionary of Land Surveyors*; 1979. Ed. P. Eden. Wm Dawson & Sons. Folkestone.
66 D/DP P16.
67 D/DW P2.
68 D/DW P1.
69 D/DW E4.
70 D/DW P3.
71 D/DQ 43/2. A modern copy of Eyre's map.
72 Information kindly supplied by Dr J. Andrews, Trinity College, Dublin.
73 C. Shrimpton, 1965. *"The landed society and the farming community of Essex in the late 18th and early 19th century.* (Ph.D. Cambridge).
74 D/DDc E4/1.
75 An anonymous undated map of Du Cane's estate purchased in 1751 is titled "A Survey of the Lordship and Parish of Great Braxted", a formula used by Donnelly for his Epping map. The Braxted map is thought to be a copy of an earlier map that, possibly, was made by Donnelly.
76 D/DBh P1.
77 Map in the GLC Record Office.
78 Map in the archives of the Marquis of Salisbury.
79 D/DM P5.
80 D/DSo P3.
81 A. S. Mason & P. Barber (in preparation).
82 This book is in the British Library.
83 Information kindly supplied by J. Bensusan-Butt.
84 Q/RRo 1/5.
85 Advertisement in the *Chelmsford Chronicle.*
86 His will is in the ERO.
87 Rebow married the daughter of Matthew Martin whose Alresford estate was surveyed by Brasier in 1730. Perhaps Brasier was not available in 1734 to work for Rebow. However, Martin, as a sea captain, might have known Rush as a local teacher of navigation.
88 D/DP P37.

89 See ref. 57 and advertisements in the *Ipswich Journal*.
90 D/DR P26.
91 D/DU 497/71.
92 D/DU 177/103.
93 D/DHt P10.
94 T/M 286.
95 Agnis's will is in ERO.
96 D/DBr P12.
97 Acc. 7920.
98 T/A 225/17.
99 D/DK P4.
100 D/D 751/178.
101 T/M 523/2.
102 T/M 523/1.
104 T/M 3.
105 D/DNF 1/1/2.
106 D/DGe P7.
107 D/DP P18.
108 D/DU 56/1.
109 Felsted Map in Map Library, British Library (ERO T/M 79); Gr. Leighs map T/M 55.
110 D/DGe P7.
111 D/DFa P2.
112 Map in Map Library, British Library.
113 D/DHw L18.
114 D/DFg P1/1–26.
115 Maps in Dept. of Manuscripts, British Library.
116 Maps and those of 1821 survey in Gwent Record Office.
117 D/DC 27/1126.
118 D/DC 27/1125.
119 D/DWe P15/1–6.
120 J. Berridge; 1942. *Essex Review 51*, 204.
121 D/DQ 71/1.
122 D/DU 28/61.
123 D/DQ 50/1.
124 D/DCm P13.
125 Original map of this survey (dated 1724) is in Southend Museum. A draft map of the survey "taken in the years 1724 and 1725" is ERO D/Dmg P1.
126 The maps are in Southend Museum.
127 D/DRa 247.
128 T/M 65/14.
129 T/M 191.
130 D/DHh P5.
131 T/M 272.
132 Map in private hands.
133 D/DMy 15M50/89.
134 D/DM P6.
135 T/M 162.
136 Map in private hands.
137 D/DB P44.
138 D/DWv P5.
139 D/DQ 71/2.
140 T/M 95.
141 D/DRa 247.
142 D/DHt P6.
143 D/DHt P4.
144 D/DBr P13.
145 D/DB P18.
146 D/DB P20.
147 T/M 127. Original map in Map Library, British Library.
148 D/DFa P4.

149 D/DHt P4.
150 D/DQh 6.
151 Map in Guildhall Library.
152 T/M 393. Original map in Leyton Library.
153 D/DW P7.
154 D/DU 417/8.
155 Information kindly supplied by Dr Peter Eden.
156 D/DSa 150.
157 D/DP 292/12/14.
158 D/DW P4.
159 D/DCw P7. This map is undated and unsigned but in style clearly by Cradock.
160 D/DCw P2–6.
161 D/DMy 17M55/5.

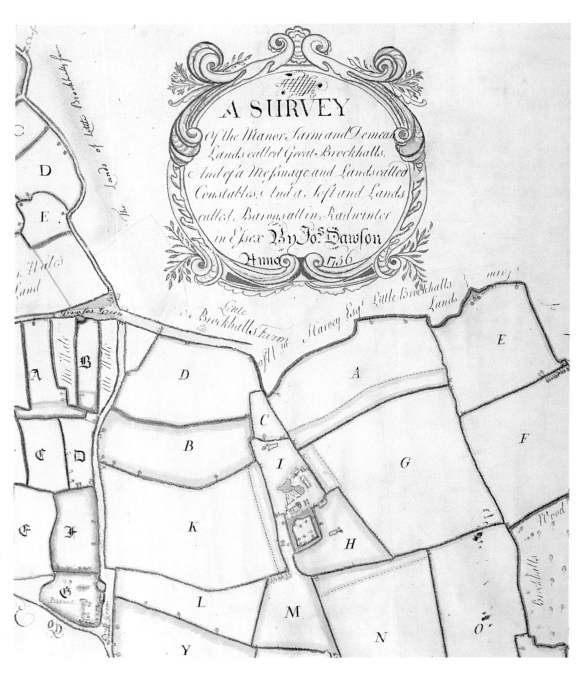

Cartouche and detail from a map of Great Brockhalls, Radwinter by Joseph Dawson (see p. 80), 1756. Note the moat and buildings in the archiac but still often used "collapsed elevation".

A beautifully executed floral cartouche by John Lee (see p. 50), 1726. The border is of an unusual delicacy. Compare Kendall's more robust treatment in the same year (p. 55).

162 D/DMy 17M55/6.

163 D/DMy 15M50/430.

164 D/DGe P5.

165 D/DQy P1.

166 After the Jacobite rebellion of 1715 all Roman Catholics had to register their estates. Stane signed the necessary certificate which is in his papers. Coffyn and Parker with Lord Petre and others have their estates recorded in Q/RRp (ERO). See *Essex Recusant 2*, 16 and later volumes for additional information on local Roman Catholics.

167 Papers regarding Stane and his will are in D/DC 27/710–18a.

168 D/DGs P35.

169 Papers relating to Mary Coffyn and her estate are in D/DHt T211/1–12.

170 D/DQp.

171 T/M 142. Original map is in Southend Museum.

172 The maps of Lord Petre's woods are bound in one volume, in the ERO (D/DP P76/1–9).

173 D/DP P22.

174 D/DP 100/3/1.

175 With the Cole-Parker maps in the Petre archive is an anonymous map of 1727 depicting Imphy manor, Buttsbury. It is totally different from the Cole style. It has a border like a picture frame, clear roman scripts and buildings drawn in block plan, a style in advance of its time. Why Petre did not employ Cole or Parker for this survey is a mystery, as is the name of the cartographer.

176 The map with its addition is in the archives of St Bartholomew's Hospital.

177 D/DPz 14/10. A list of Lord Petre's servants at Thorndon, dated 1742.

178 D/DP P23/1.

179 D/DTw P1.

180 Plans in the Map Library, British Library.

181 D/DBy P1, and map at Audley End. For discussion see *The Landscape of Audley End*, 1983. Land Use Consultants. Rocque and Dubois were Huguenots; Bourginion may well have been one.

182 D/DB P54.

183 The two maps and the Charterhouse catalogue are in the GLC Record Office.

SECOND PERIOD (1735–69)

Surveyors From
outside Essex

LONDON BASED

JAMES CROW seems to have been a partnership man. His work as Thomas Browne's assistant in 1749 has been described and is a reminder that in this period of time Browne was still an active and important surveyor.

Although London-based, Crow was an Essex man. In 1749 he told the Commissioners of the Chancery Court that he was "of the parish of St Andrew, Holborn" and 37 years old. He stated[1] that he was well qualified to survey in Thurrock as he knew the land, "for many years past having heretofore lived in or near the said parish". But his only survey on his own was in 1747 so that, given his age and the fact that his London address was the same as that given by Browne, it is likely that his early career was as an anonymous assistant to Browne.

Crow's 1747 survey[2] was of the 1000 acre Dagnams estate which comprised almost the whole parish of Noak Hill, near Romford. This estate had been in the possession of the Carteret family and visited by Samuel Pepys. Carteret died in 1739, when a brief written survey[3] of the estate was made. Crow's title for his 1747 map got as far as ". . . being the estate of . . ." and then left a blank space. The map is neatly set out with clear scripts. It is interesting that Crow did not survey the timber. That was done in the same year by Thomas Davis "Timber and land surveyor" of Godalming, Surrey.[4] This survey was done before Crow measured the land as it lists "a new cutt wood, the name not known". This wood is marked on Crow's map as "Elmwood".

Crow's subsequent Essex work was as co-surveyor with THOMAS MARSH. Marsh had surveyed alone in Kent from 1750 onwards but was together with Crow working in Hertfordshire[5] in 1762 and 1764.

Their work in Essex started in 1767 when they surveyed[6] the 1200 acre estate of John Goodere in South Ockendon. They were back the next year in that area, judging from an anonymous sketch map[7] of an Aveley farm "surveyed by James Crow and Thomas Marsh". Their really major work in Essex was the 1771 survey[8] of Lord Grimston's large estate covering over 2000 acres in Bergholt, Pebmarsh, Bradfield, Mistley and Wix. The size of their commissions makes it obvious that together they were an important team of London surveyors. Their maps are rather plain, do not show land usage and have conventional rococo cartouches. As cartographers they were not inspired.

Marsh's own work in Essex consisted of a survey[9] for Lord Archer of 563 acres in Southchurch in 1776 and an undated survey of about the same time of an estate in Fyfield.[10] His last Essex work[11] was a minor affair of scattered land in Fobbing that amounted to only 63 acres. Both Marsh and Crow surveyed in many counties and were obviously a successful London team willing to travel.

EDWARD JOHN EYRE was, for Essex, the prime example of a full-time London based surveyor who travelled widely, a type coming to the fore towards the middle of the century. Eyre's work in Essex was characteristically concerned with major surveys, often for institutions. In 1751 Eyre surveyed the whole parish of Epping.[12] A cartouche of piled books and attendant cherubs frames the words "John Conyers, Copt Hall Essex". This has led to the speculation on page 41 that Eyre may have been responsible for the copy of Donnelly's 1719 Epping map, the copy being made for Conyers.

Eyre's career took him to most of the southern counties and in to Wales, but he was back in Essex in 1757, and fully engaged there in the next year. His plan[13] of Audley End house and gardens made in 1757 followed a similar survey in 1753 by Francis Warren of Suffolk. In 1758 Eyre surveyed and mapped[14] the town of Saffron Walden, and also surveyed the whole manor of Walden. From this survey he made seven maps[15] of the farms and combined them into one large map[16] "authenticated by the Presentment of the Jury made at a Court of Survey". The Audley End estate was then in the hands of the Countess of Portsmouth and in a pretty parlous state, the "neat profit" being only £140-6-6 in 1759.[17]

By contrast to his usual large surveys Eyre, also in 1752, mapped[18] a 30 acre farm in Baddow. This very minor work does not appear to be a survivor from a larger project. The map is in the Mildmay archive and the family was in the habit of using local Essex surveyors.

A notebook[19] containing a written "Survey of the Bounds of the Parish of Clavering with several farms in the Parishes of Clavering and Burden . . . taken in the year 1762 by Edwd John Eyre, Land Surveyor" details the lands held by Christ's Hospital and explains the two anonymous undated maps[20] of Clavering and Langley in the Hospital's archive. The maps are typical of Eyre's cartography. Both maps show in detail the parish boundary. Scattered over the large blank space contained within the boundary are the lands belonging to the Hospital.

The boundaries are not only drawn in great detail, they also show the various trees used as boundary marks, giving the six species of tree involved. Using these large maps it would be easy to perambulate the two parishes without taking a step. Why the Hospital wanted these unusual maps is not made clear by the Minute Book of the Hospital.[21] During 1762 there were the continuing tithe disputes that were endemic in many estates. More relevant is the record of Thomas Wolfe, the Hospital's agent for its Essex estates, being thanked and dismissed as the Hospital authorities decided to take over the estate management.

The year 1762 was Eyre's year for Essex as he crossed the county to survey[22] the Earl of Rochford's park and gardens in St Osyth. He would have used his London base for his diminished version[23] of Daniel Halls' 1723 map of Mowden Hall in Hatfield Peverel. *Illustration, page 42*

Eyre's last Essex commission was from New College, Oxford. On these maps he put "Survey'd, valued and plan'd", which shows the importance of valuation in a land surveyor's expertise. He added various comments on the land, such as "The salts is a very coarse piece of land yielding little or no profit." In 1767 Eyre completed and delivered to the College maps of its lands in Takeley (687 a.) and Widdington[24] (333 a.). The last year of Eyre's career is given as 1767 in the Dictionary of Surveyors but in 1984 three further maps of the New College series appeared and were added to the College's archives. These maps[25] by Eyre are dated 1768 and show the College's lands in Dunmow (688 a.), Bradwell (848 a.) and Writtle (300 a.). As there is no record of these maps having been received by New College at the time that they were made, it is very possible that Eyre died after completing this work but before he could deliver it.

Eyre's cartography was remarkable for its clarity and fine penmanship. His scripts are like the best typefaces, well away from the earlier decorative writing. Many of his maps are covered with a grid, with reference letters along the borders. His cartouches were monochrome and of a simple rococo design. The cartouches of his two maps for Christ's Hospital enclose a blank space; he never got round to writing a title. This does indicate that cartographers often drew the cartouche first and then added the title, a habit that is obvious in the several estate maps

*A fine floral cartouche
by William Woodward
(see p. 66), 1769,
demonstrating the more
delicate palette used in
decoration in the second
half of the century.*

where the title spreads over parts of the cartouche. Eyre dealt with outlying parcels of land by enclosing them with a hint of a scroll or the curled edge of a piece of paper. His work is a splendid example of how clear presentation of information was itself artistic and needed no further decoration. Yet he could be romantic and floridly stylish as in his map of Lord Rochford's park. In this his polar indicator is a decorated wheel with cherub faces blowing the four winds. An elaborate rococo cartouche incorporates garden tools. That Eyre was an artist is also evident from the engravings[26] of Lord Chesterfield's London houses made from Eyre's drawings.

*Illustrations
pages 105 and 106*

WILLIAM WOODWARD was a pupil of Eyre's and, like his master, settled in Lincoln's Inn Fields. It is a pity that he made only one Essex survey, for his cartography was so beautiful. His 1769 map[27] of a farm in Runwell has the clear fine scripts of Eyre and the same plain scale and compass rose. The boundaries are shown with elegant detail, the arable land is indicated with neat "furrows" and the trees are well drawn. Woodward followed Eyre in the type of cartouche but added the most beautiful flowers, so well drawn and coloured that they bear comparison with a naturalistic flower picture. This is an extraordinary combination of restrained elegance that became the feature of estate maps in the 1770s and lyrical flower painting.

*Illustration,
page 66*

A coincidence of name and profession links William Woodward with JOHN WOODWARD who made his one Essex survey[28] in 1742. This was a major work, embracing the 1240 acres of

Sir Hildebrand Jacob's estate in Halstead, Earls Colne and Colne Engayne. The cartography is crude and somewhat archaic for the time. Under the scale bar is a very odd geometric squared pattern that may have been the best decoration that John Woodward could draw. Given the dates and the probability that he was a London surveyor (his work was in London and the home counties) it is possible that he was the father of William Woodward but did not have his son's talents.

JAMES BERMINGHAM and JOHN NOBLE are linked by time, similarity of clients and Noble's map of a Bermingham survey. Bermingham's major work in Essex was for the Commissioners of Sewers. For them he made his first Essex survey in 1735, presenting the

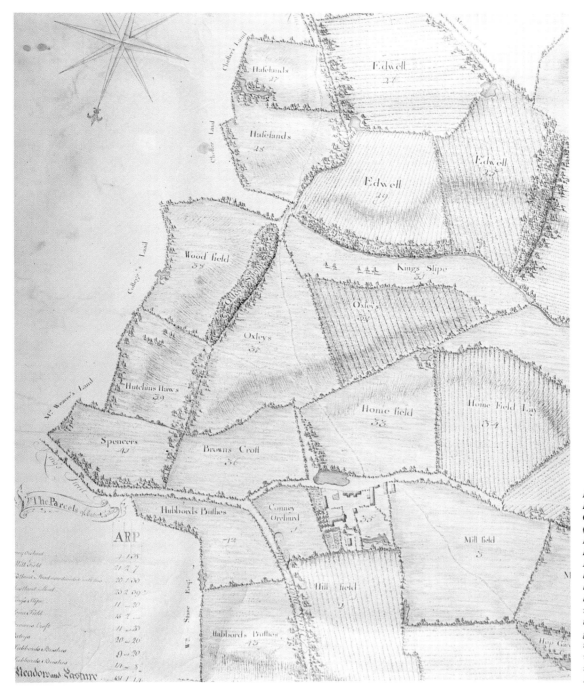

Detail from a map of Parsfield Hall, High Ongar by John Rocque (see p. 71), 1741. Rocque made few English estate maps. Note the use of "plough-lines" to indicate arable land and the fine hatching to indicate the relief of the land, a technique which was to gain wider currency later in the century and ultimately to find a place in the first Ordnance Survey maps.

marshland of the contiguous Havering and Dagenham Levels in two maps.[29] The maps are identical in style with the title written in huge red and black roman capitals set in a grey frame of cartouche. Richard Gough in 1780 noted a folio sheet[30] that gave a "particular account of decreed lands in the Levels of Dagenham and Havering . . . as per map taken from Mr Bermingham's survey anno 1735".

Stuck into the Presentment Book of the Commissioners of Sewers is a memorandum,[31] dated 1 May 1740, written in a rather crabbed hand by Bermingham, who gave his address as Duke Street, Bloomsbury. The memorandum is a contract between the Commissioners and Bermingham, who promised to "truly and correctly measure map and plan the Levels of Havering, Dagenham, Ripple, Barking, East Ham, Leyton, Walthamstow, Bromley and East marsh in 18 months "excepting capacitated by sickness . . . or basness of Wether". He computed the whole area to be about 6000 acres and stated that he would correct any error free of charge. He further agreed to pay a penalty of £100 if he defaulted on the contract.

It is not clear why the Havering and Dagenham levels were mentioned in the contract. The 1735 maps are the only indication of Bermingham's work. In 1740 he produced three maps[32] covering the Barking area of marshland. A small area of East Ham was mapped[33] in 1741 and the very large area of East Ham marshes was mapped[34] in that year by John Noble from Bermingham's survey. Maps for the Levels in West Ham, Leyton, Walthamstow and Bromley do not exist; these Levels were then in the county of Middlesex. The area for which maps exist accounts for about 60% of the computed total of 6000 acres.

It is interesting that Bermingham charged seven pence an acre for this survey, without claiming any expenses. Presumably he must have paid Noble for making his map out of the £95 or so that he received. In 1737 Bermingham surveyed the Guy's Hospital estate[35] (709 a.) in Felsted and charged six pence an acre, but added £4-0-6 "for taking account of all the timber trees, saplings and pollards."[36]

Illustration, page 51

In 1738 he surveyed 32 acres in Dagenham[37] and 23 acres in Ilford,[38] the latter for Gascoyne. Then, in 1740 he surveyed for Dr Bamber, Gascoyne's son-in-law, of St Bartholomew's Hospital, 260 acres of farm land in Tillingham[39] and 57 acres in Chigwell.[40]

Bermingham's cartography was tidy. He used little colour, having monochrome classical cartouches, except for his minor maps on which he set the title on a mantle. His scripts were clear, with good roman capitals. Apart from his Essex work, he surveyed in Berkshire and Oxfordshire, ending his career in 1745.

John Noble's first Essex work was the mapping of Bermingham's survey of East Ham marshes (1741, 1666 a.) For Lethieullier he surveyed (1748) his manor of Aldersbrooke,[41] showing some land measured for Gascoyne by Bermingham, and also mapped[42] "an ancient entrenchment in Barking", displaying the title on a mantle. The Bamber/Gascoyne links are obvious in his map[43] for Dr Bamber (c. 1745) of 40 acres in Dagenham and his work for St Bartholomew's Hospital in 1748. At that time the Hospital's country estates were directly administered by a small group drawn from the large number of Governors.[44] The Essex estates were looked after by "Alderman Gascoyne". In the autumn of 1746 he visited every Essex holding, seeing to rents, repairs and management. He found a neglected farmhouse with the land over-ploughed and praised a farmer for using his land "in an husbandlike manner". In December of that year he recommended that "plans be taken of the farms in Essex . . . that are not already planned". As a result Noble surveyed and mapped[45] the Hospital's estates in Layer Marney (261 a.) and Steeple St Lawrence (1225 a.).

Noble loved a vividly coloured painted cartouche with a floral theme, using this design for all his major maps. His scripts and layout are a little untidy compared with Bermingham's style. There is no record of Noble surveying in any English county apart from Essex. He disappeared from the English scene after 1748. However, a John Noble turns up to survey in Dublin in 1749 and went on to survey Co. Kildare, making the first Irish county map on a scale of one inch to one mile.[46]

THOMAS BATEMAN of Holborn made one Essex survey, in 1767. His map[47] is a remarkable mixture of "picture map" and "scale survey" as defined and discussed by P. D. A. Harvey in his book *Topographical Maps*.[48] The map is of "Poorfleet farm" (373 a.) and pictures the extensive chalk pits of Purfleet with their steep sides and irregular bottom on which two smoking lime kilns are drawn. The picture is a bird's eye view showing the natural appearance of the land. To the side of this picture the buildings are shown in block plan and the rest of the map is a "flat" survey to strict scale. The whole effect is most pleasing and graced by a cartouche of complex rococo design festooned with flowers.

Illustration, page 58

Bateman worked in the home counties from 1754 to 1771, the Duke of Bedford being a client. Parts of Francis Tyson's Hackney estate were surveyed by Bateman in 1764 and 5, but in 1768 another part was surveyed by Mackoun. All these maps[49] are known only from copies of 1837.

JOHN MACKOUN is placed as a Londoner solely because of his association with Bateman in Hackney. "A Survey of part of the estate belonging to Francis John Tyson . . . in the Parish of Hackney . . . surveyed by J. Mackoun 1768" was "copied from the original" by George Hawkins in 1837. Mackoun's major surveys in 1769 and 1770 of the south Cambridgeshire parishes of Horseheath and West Wickham are known only from traced copies.[50] It is disappointing that a man with such skill, as is evident from his one surviving original survey, should have left so little trace of a career.

In 1766 Mackoun surveyed the "Estate of John Barrington Esq. and Lands by Inheritance and Acquisitions by Purchase Belonging to Mr Stephen Wilson". The 5463 acre estate lay mainly in Hatfield Broadoak but extended in to Matching, Aythorpe Roding, Stansted, White Roding and Takeley. The book of maps[51] that "delineates" this survey shows Mackoun's cartography, in its detailed layout and artistry, to be of the highest quality, closely rivalling the skills of P. B. Scalé so beautifully demonstrated by his 1778 maps of Mistley. Both Scalé and Mackoun use a similar decorated script for their title page. Mackoun's title page is framed with a light rococo design embellished by well drawn mathematical instruments. He drew 48 maps, each rich in detail. There are deer in the park and swans on the lake. Gates, stiles, hedges and fences are shown as they looked. Each map has a page of reference, listing acreage, tenant, quality (i.e. pasture, arable or wood), the value per acre and the value per annum (not filled in). The page numbers and each polar indicator are well decorated. At the back of this leather bound book are pages ruled into columns for rents and land tax, but no figures have been put in. The book shows that Mackoun had valued as well as measured the land and allowed for the book to be a document for estate management. It looks as if the beauty of the cartography made Barrington reserve it for the glances of admiring friends.

Illustration, page 21

Illustration, page 34

An intriguing large map[52] is "A plan of the parish of King's Hatfield otherwise Hatfield Broadoak drawn from the surveys of Jn° Mackoun taken in the year 1766". At first glance this might be taken to be a map made by Mackoun in 1766 (it is catalogued under that date) to supplement his book of maps. Such a combination of one large map and a book of maps was not uncommon. However the map itself is not dated and has two sets of reference letters on the fields shown. The red letters on Barrington's fields refer to Mackoun's reference letters in his book of maps. But the parish lands outside Barrington's holdings have grey numbers that refer to a written survey,[53] "The account of lands in the Parish of Hatfield Regis . . . that are not part of the estates of John Barrington . . . as by admeasurement in the years 1779 and 1780". The key to this survey observes that the numbers in the first column are references to lands laid down in the general plan. The survey ends with a summary of Barrington's lands followed by "that part of Mr Mackoun's account to be added to the quantity of acres in the whole parish". Therefore the map was drawn to illustrate the 1779 and 1780 written survey of parish lands to which was added Barrington's lands in the same parish according to Mackoun's survey of 1766. The map itself is well drawn with an elegant penmanship, and its maker must have been the man who did the later survey. Fortunately he put his name at the end of the survey, "surveyed by John Sanders 1779 and 1780". Sanders lived at Bishop's Stortford and his details are recorded in the last section of this study.

To add spice to this little problem is one sheet of an uncompleted map[54] on which is written "A plan of Hatfield Broadoak, 1778". Field boundaries are just sketched in, but they correspond exactly with the lower part of Sanders' map, being on the same scale. The only complete part of the map is an elaborate grey cartouche with a fantastic arch with an urn on top and double classical columns on either side entwined by leafy tendrils. The cartouche is empty (the title and date being roughly written at the bottom of the sheet) and is another example (see Eyre's maps for Christ's Hospital) of the cartographer creating the finished cartouche before contemplating writing the title within it. The obvious guess is that this fragment of a parish map was an early and abandoned attempt by Sanders.

SAMUEL DRIVER surveyed the 800 acre manor of Stifford[55] in 1762. The map has a well executed conventional classical cartouche of flowers and foliage. The unusual decorations are the pollarded trees framing the tables of contents and the curious chained pheasant between two felled trees above the scale bar. His other Essex work[56] is intriguing. "Mr Driver's sketch for a garden at Belhus, 1764" hints at Driver trying to be a landscape gardener. But the sketch

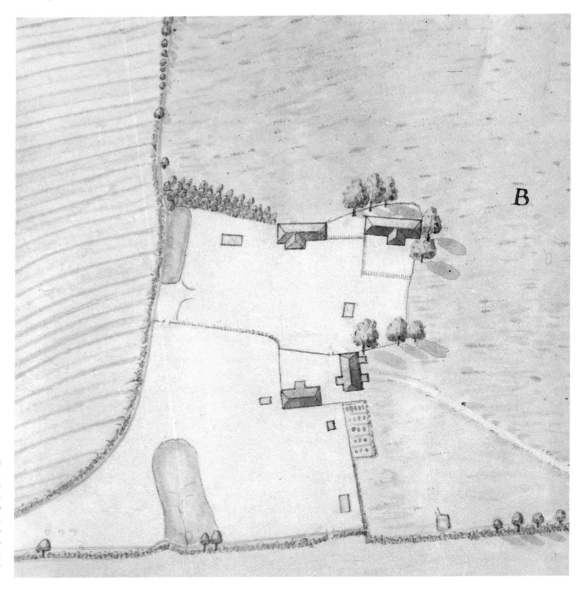

Detail from a map of a farm in Latchingdon, 1723, by the French military engineer, John Thomas (see p.42). Note the buildings, shown strictly in plan and the use of shading on the roofs and shadows on trees and hedges to give "depth" to the map.

merely shows a grove of trees or shrubs set against the words "house" and "stable yard" to indicate the site. Belhus was Lord Dacre's seat at Aveley and at that time Dacre was full of plans to embellish it with the help of Capability Brown.[57] These plans were frustrated by his lordship's lack of cash and health, although Richard Woods was to do some later work on the park. Driver's intervention seems irrelevant to the main plans.

Samuel Driver (1720–79) is known best as the progenitor of a dynasty of surveyors. His father, also Samuel (1692–1741) was a baker and market gardener of Wandsworth who took to survey and valuation but not land measurement. His uncle Charles was a surveyor in Rotherhythe. The Samuel Driver of the Stifford survey acquired by marriage a market and nursery garden in the Old Kent Road, which the family looked after until their surveying business became paramount in 1802. The Essex equivalent to Samuel Driver was George Sangster, who ran a nursery garden in Brentwood and was a land surveyor. Both Samuel Driver's sons were surveyors, and one, Abraham, had sons who continued this business. The Drivers played a major part in the 19th century to form surveyors into a professional body. The dynasty continues today in the London firm of chartered surveyors, Drivers Jonas. The firm celebrated its 250th anniversary in 1975 with the publication of its history.[58]

As any book on cartography will testify, JOHN ROCQUE was a prolific cartographer, engraver and map-seller in London.[59] He was also the leading 18th century surveyor of British cities, notably London (a massive survey from 1737 to 1747). A refugee Huguenot, he set up in London as a designer of gardens, when his brother Bartholomew started his own gardening business. In 1734–7 Rocque published engraved plans of gardens belonging to the rich and famous, including plans of Lord Tylney's grounds of Wanstead Place.[60]

Although Rocque surveyed some counties, his work as an estate surveyor in England was limited to an estate at Walton on Thames[61] (1744) and Lord Tylney's farm of Parsfield Hall, High Ongar,[62] in 1741. The baroque cartouche of this map is drawn in line without elaboration, its frame topped by a coat of arms and supporting two well drawn human figures, one female, with headdress, holding a spear, the other a male holding a trident. The hedgerows and fields are shown naturalistically, the arable with furrows, and the elevation of the land is indicated by shading. The title is written in good Roman capitals and the rest of the script is like a good typeface.

Illustration, page 67

A feature of this map is the filling of three spaces at the bottom with tables of contents in sloping script and decorated by a pink ribbon. The tables, not by Rocque, list pasture, wood and tillage. Their creator is obvious by the note that "The contents of the fields were ascertained from this map and the tillage, meadow, pasture and wood from a view of the farm by John Storer in 1776". Storer of Halstead often used "pink ribbon" decoration. His "view" of the farm, rather than new measurement and a new map, was a common part of a land surveyor's work. The working life of many estate maps was very long, later corrections and additions being imposed on them.

By 1753 Rocque was flourishing in output, if not in profit. He employed five draftsmen and five surveyors. At this point he left his London business to continue without him and went to Dublin, a city that he then surveyed. But in Ireland he became the chief land surveyor of estates. The five volumes of his maps that cover the vast estates of the Earl of Kildare are the finest examples of 18th century estate cartography. Their elegant style is way above and quite different from his 1741 map of Ongar. Rocque took with him as an apprentice his young brother in law, Bernard Scalé, whose sister, the widow Bew née Scalé, Rocque had taken as his second wife in 1751. It may be that Scalé was the decorator of these maps (see page 124). Rocque returned to England, his last surveys being of Irish estates in 1760, and died in poverty in 1762, although his London business was carried on successfully by his widow Mary Ann Rocque.

The small glebe of Little Ilford was surveyed[63] in 1737 by a J. Bland. Presumably this was JOSEPH BLAND, known for his association with Warburton in the production of the latter's map of Middlesex, Hertfordshire and Essex. This was first proposed in 1720 and the first edition ready in 1725. According to Donald Hodson,[64] the role of Joseph Bland was as a collector of subscriptions and not as a surveyor, the surveys being done by Payling Smith. The map of the Ilford glebe is crude and undecorated.

CHARLES SLOANE, "Junior of Wardour Street", as he put on his 1761 map[65] of an estate in Great Bardfield, had previously been a surveyor from Kent. He was the son of Charles Sloane of Gravesend and had worked with his father. The Bardfield map was made for the London Company of Haberdashers. The map, accompanied by a written survey, is remarkably poor considering the high reputation of the family.

London instrument makers and mathematicians made no significant contribution to Essex surveys during this period. NATHANIEL HILL, who flourished in Chancery Lane from the 1740s to 1760, mapped[66] in 1742 the portion of Mary Weldale's Barking marshes that had not been shown on Wyeth's map of 1735. It is of note that James Bermingham was at that time busily surveying much of that marshland for the Commissioners of Sewers. Hill's neat plain map curiously lacks a scale bar.

Hill also surveyed the Bedford Level in the Fens together with Tycho Wing, the partner and brother-in-law of Thomas Heath. THOMAS HEATH was one of the best known of the many instrument makers who were freemen of the Grocers' Company. A Nathaniel Hill was apprenticed in the Company in 1701 but left before gaining his freedom.

Heath's only Essex survey[67] was of Woodford Wood, measured in acres and customary wood measure in 1757. The cartouche is baroque in a rather simple fashion. The wood belonged to the Earl of Tylney (the Childs family), spelled by Heath as "Tinley", not the way to guarantee a satisfied customer.

In London at this time the Office of Ordnance was using its own surveyors and draftsmen mainly for laying out plans of fortifications or of the lands where these would be built. This work is outside the scope of a text devoted to land surveyors. However, as an indication of what went on, there are two maps of Harwich, one dated[68] 1745 and the other undated[69] but from about that year. The 1745 map shows the whole parish of Harwich with the title "His Majesty's Lands, Messuages, Stables and other buildings purchased by Act of Parliament for Fortifying Harwich". The survey by a warrant from the Surveyor General was carried out by Griffith Davies. For the King's lands and forests the Surveyor General usually commissioned a freelance land surveyor, but in this case nothing else is known of Davies and it is likely that he was employed by the Ordnance for the undated map of Harwich showing the "Town of Harwich with the Boundary of the King's Land" which was copied by Tho. Chamberlain at the Office of Ordnance Drawing Room.

MEN FROM KENT

TWO KENT SURVEYORS just scrape into this time period, making a total of six working in Essex from 1700 to 1739. After that there is a gap of 34 years before another man comes from Kent to Essex (in 1773). However, apart from Skynner's survey in Greenwich (1745), Essex surveyors did not work in Kent. It is probably stating the obvious to observe that most of the London surveyors who worked in Essex in the first two-thirds of the century also worked in Kent.

JOHN BOWRA, early on in his career, went up to Toppesfield in 1738 to survey[70] two farms inherited by a resident of Kent. In 1729 "John Crane of Sturry, Kent, Clerk, cousin and co-heir of Robert Clerk late of Wethersfield, Gent." took over the two farms and also a house in West Street, Harwich, "heretofore used for a hospital for sick and wounded seamen and sometimes afterwards for a meeting house".

Bowra's map is in early 18th century style with a broad border decorated with a "continuous vine" motif, a grey baroque cartouche and an "explanation" set on a red mantle tied with knotted ribbons. The polar indicator is an intricate coloured multistar device. Bowra was born in Sevenoaks in 1714 and later worked from Tonbridge. He died in 1780. Dr Hull[71] judges him as a surveyor of distinction.

JARED HILL, of Canterbury, was part of a family of surveyors in that city. In 1738 he surveyed[72] the Chingford estate (587 a.) of Robert Boothby. The Boothbys were the most important family in Chingford (the map shows their achievement of arms) but Robert was born in 1735, the year in which his father died. Robert's mother then rapidly married Benjamin Moyer, for whom Hill surveyed[73] 69 a. in Leyton in 1739. Very probably Moyer, on behalf of his new wife, had commissioned Hill's survey of the Boothby estate. In 1739 Hill also surveyed[74] 94 acres scattered around Walthamstow, and belonging to Richard Collard, probably while in the vicinity for the Moyer survey. Jared Hill surveyed fairly widely, from Sussex to Suffolk, so his trips to south-west Essex were not unique.[75]

MEN FROM HERTFORDSHIRE

THE YEAR 1746 was the first year in which a Hertfordshire surveyor worked in Essex. In that year JEREMIAH HELDER surveyed for the Free School of Cheshunt, Herts, its estates in Clavering, Arkesden, Langley and Elmdon. These scattered lands, totalling about 200 acres, were shown on two maps.[76] Undated anonymous copies of these maps,[77] together with a terrier of the estate and other documents, were held by a long established firm of solicitors in Waltham Abbey. The rest of Helder's work appears to have been confined to Hertfordshire, from 1710 to 1746.

Elaborate monochrome cartouche by Daniel Mumford (see p. 100), 1796. The ability to draw on a wide range of lettering styles was viewed as a mark of sophistication in map representation.

JOHN ELLIS of Whetstone near Barnet surveyed widely around the home counties. In 1755, early in his career, he measured a small parcel of land in Havering. His map[78] has no title and is probably only a draft.

HOLLINGWORTH and LANDERS (without initials) surveyed and mapped[79] Takely forest in the parish of Hatfield Broadoak for Jacob Houblon in 1757. The map bears the arms of Cotton, a neat compliment to Mrs Houblon, who was a Miss Cotton before her marriage. The grey wash cartouche is floridly rococo but the polar indicator is a plain cross. The contents table is flanked by two classical columns, as on the map[80] of 78 acres scattered around Chishall made in 1769 by J. Hollingworth. This may have been the maker of the Takely forest map. The style for both maps is similar. The forest map has a detailed drawing of the elevation of the "Shell House"

and the Chishall map has very detailed perspective drawings of the churches and a windmill. However the Chishall map might have been made by the son, John Hollingworth of Puckeridge, Herts, whose later work is described in the next section. In 1774 an advertisement[81] by "Hollingworth & Co." stated that they were continuing the business of Mr Hollingworth, late father". As the name Landers is only to be found on the Takely forest map, it is possible that Landers as a surveyor was the "& Co." of Hollingworth & Co.

FROM NORTH OF ESSEX

THE FIRST SUFFOLK surveyor to work in 18th century Essex was JOHN MILLER of Hadleigh, Suffolk. In 1735 he surveyed[82] a 746 acre estate in Layer de la Haye, in 1750 he mapped[83] a small estate in Birch and then, in 1757, came further south to map,[84] in Witham, the "Estate of James Glanvill Gentleman a minor by the order of Richard G. Glanville Esquire the acting Executor to the late Rev. James Husband". It is possible that Glanvill was a Suffolk man. There is nothing remarkable about these three sparsely decorated but neat maps. Apart from these excursions to Essex, Miller's long career (1718–57) was spent working in Suffolk and Norfolk.

FRANCIS WARREN came to Saffron Walden in 1752 to map[85] a small farm of Mr Ingrey's. Perhaps it was during that visit that he surveyed Audley End park, although the map[86] is dated 1753. The map for Mr Ingrey is on a roller. The title is written in big plain capitals across the top, with no cartouche. The compass star is gilded with a grey flower at its centre. The state of cultivation is shown in the table of contents and the boundaries are drawn in colours to distinguish ownership. In short, a neat useful map.

Francis Warren was related to the well known Bury St. Edmunds father and son team of Thomas Warren, senior and junior. Francis may well have been the brother of the senior Thomas; both were co-surveyors of a Suffolk estate[87] in 1729.

There are several intriguing points about Francis Warren's trip to Audley End. First, it appears to have been his only work outside Suffolk; second, 1752 was the year when the Countess of Portsmouth bought Audley End, and, last, E. J. Eyre surveyed the whole area including Audley End only five years later. But the Warren family had some hold on Audley End, as the younger Thomas surveyed it in 1783.

THOMAS HALL of Debenham is notable only for achieving the double of surveying Suffolk land for an Essex client and Essex land for a Suffolk man. In 1739 he surveyed the 105 acre estate in Copford and Birch belonging to Mr Season of Ipswich, and made a plain map[88] enlivened by a colourful compass rose. His Debenham survey[89] (1737) was of land owned by a Harwich widow.

THOMAS SPENCER of Wickhambrook is known only for surveying the estate of Edward Coldham that lay around Haverhill. The Suffolk portion was mapped[90] in 1766 and the Essex portion[91] (240 a.) in 1767. This map, which includes Haverhill hamlet, is attractive with a gilded cartouche festooned with red flowers.

JOHN PRITTY is placed as a Suffolk surveyor because of his known work in that county[92] in the years 1746, 1748, 1750 and 1777. His work in Essex was confined to 1759. In that year he surveyed the Woodham Mortimer estate[93] of a Maldon resident and some of the Beeleigh Abbey lands in Maldon.[94] The latter map has a note stating that the land was remeasured in 1771 by "Mr Hall of Maldon". Both maps are crudely executed and undistinguished.

BRIDGE BAYNES, quoted as only surveying in Suffolk, mapped a nine acre parcel in Bocking for Joseph Savill of that town. He made a meal of it by producing a map[95] (dated

1756) at a scale of 40 inches to a mile, and using brightly coloured boundaries and an over-large compass star.

Two names associated with Cambridgeshire come into this list. ROBERT CHAPMAN is quoted as "heretofore of Burrough Green, Cambs." in 1741, and is said to have surveyed in Suffolk.[96] In Essex he surveyed a property in Woodham Ferris, mapped in the 1760s by Skynner when he was both surveying and making maps of old surveys for Strutt. The property surveyed by Chapman was bought by Strutt in 1741 from a Newmarket man, who presumably sent Chapman down to Essex just before the sale.

JOHN FREEMAN surveyed a small property in Dunmow in 1768. His considerable career, based on Cambridge, developed in the last 30 years of the century and will be discussed in the next section of text.

From Norfolk, in 1767, came JAMES PARKER of Thetford to survey the estate of Sir William Wake[97] in Nazeing (1051 a. on one map)[98] and nearby Waltham Cross (145 a. on two maps).[99] The maps are well drawn, the cartouches having an intricate monochrome design with a shell motif in the first two and, on the second Waltham map, a brightly coloured lighter design incorporating an animal mask. On all there is a bright compass rose placed centrally with rays spreading over the blank spaces. The two Waltham maps are mounted on rollers and enclosed in a wooden case. The second Waltham map has "of Thetford" and "Jas." Parker. On some other maps he signed himself just "J. Parker" which is somewhat confusing. His work in Essex was early in a long career of surveying in Norfolk and Suffolk, including the 700 acre estate at Horsford, Norfolk, owned by Lord Dacre of Aveley, Essex, in 1773.[100]

FROM FAR AFIELD

THE ONE ESSEX map[101] of W. FAIRCHILD is a strange affair. Made in 1760 and titled "A survey of the Parish of Shalford . . ." it depicts the lands belonging to Jones Raymond that were surveyed by Brasier in the 1730s. It is really a map set in a document, only 13 inches from top to bottom but 55 inches wide. The map is 13 by 17 inches only, flanked by massive tables of contents. The map's north-south orientation is the opposite to that of Brasier's. It is an attractive map with the Raymond arms and a delicate classical cartouche.

W. Fairchild did much survey work in Somerset during the 1760s, mainly for the Acland family. Comparison of these maps with the Shalford map shows clearly that all are by the same hand.[102] Fairchild is also quoted as surveying in Wiltshire but in no other counties than those mentioned. His career spanned from 1760 to 1784. All this prompts three thoughts about his Shalford work: 1) He originally came from London, or Essex, and started his career by working in Shalford before setting up business in Somerset, 2) he made the long journey up from Somerset to Essex, 3) he never went to Shalford but was given Brasier's work to copy; this may not be too farfetched, for Raymond was using Skynner for new surveys of his land outside Shalford in 1755 and 1758.

OF NO FIXED ABODE

THIS IS AN apt description for T. HATTON, who surveyed[103] in West Wickham, Kent, in 1753 and near Mildenhall, Suffolk[104] in 1768. His only Essex[105] map is undated and depicts the lands of Fingrinhoe Hall.

Essex Surveyors

NORTH ESSEX

SOME, WHOSE WORK has been described, were still surveying in this period of time. Nicholls' last map was dated 1742, and Agnis, after a long gap, made a map in 1756. Hayward Rush was the last of the schoolmasters still surveying in 1747, the year of his death. However the style of the Kendall family of schoolmaster/surveyors was copied by JAMES SIMPSON in 1742 on his map[106] of four farms (total 340 a.) in Great Clacton. His cartouche is almost identical with that on Joseph Kendall's map (1730) of another farm in Great Clacton. Both have a heart-shaped space for the title, lyre-shaped side decorations, a grotesque lion mask at the top and the scale bar set within the bottom of the cartouche. Either Simpson had Kendall's map before him as he drew or he had been his pupil. Nothing else is known of Simpson. The fact that he also put on his one map a drawing of a tripod holding up a plane-table suggests that he was a land surveyor as a full-time occupation.

THOMAS ALEFOUNDER surveyed Dr Blair's 465 acre estate in Little Horkesley, covering it in three maps[107] drawn in the years 1762, 1763 and 1765. This leisurely progress suggests that Alefounder earned his living in some other way than surveying. He may well have been a schoolmaster as his maps are decorated with variations of the hand and pen motif used by writing masters to illustrate their 17th century text books. Some London writing masters were to be found at "the sign of the hand and pen". Alefounder not only used the straight picture of a hand holding a quill pen in the recommended manner but also framed the title of one map with that picture and others of two hands sharpening a quill and two ink horns. His own scripts show high quality penmanship.

Illustration, page 97

Alefounder used a curious repeated tulip design to frame written comments. The comments are reminiscent of old manorial surveys recording the customs of the manor. For example, he names three men entitled to the first crop of a meadow and adds "according to the account given by James Creak, the Tenant . . . the above persons must mow down their grass and carry off the hay between the 3rd of May and the first of August or the tenant of the said farm may prevent them from coming to the said meadow by locking up the gates".

It is a pleasing conjecture that Alefounder was a schoolmaster who obliged his friend the local doctor with a survey. Apart from a note of a survey in Suffolk in 1776 there is no other record of Alefounder's work. He was alive in 1781, as Thomas Alefounder of Nayland styled himself "Junior" on a map.[108] Maybe Thomas senior was the man of that name who married Ann Tailer at St Mary's, Colchester in 1744 and later witnessed wills[109] for inhabitants of Langham. He was not the son of the Rev. John Alefounder, a late 17th century rector of Dedham, whose sons went into the Church and were not named Thomas.

R. DYER is known only from his maps. "An accurate survey"[110] of the manor of Little Yeldham, owned by Peter Muilman the historian, was made in 1766 by Dyer. The survey is in book form, containing 34 small maps, of which 19 are of single cottages drawn in perspective and one "a representation of Blacksmith's forge". The remaining maps show small parcels of land, from one to 32 acres. The book, with additions up to 1773, has a list of tenants that does not include Dyer. Nor was he the steward of the manor, as Muilman himself records a succession of three attorneys, ending with James Round of Colchester, as occupants of that office.

Dyer's only other map,[111] dated 1767, was of scattered small parcels of land (a total of 95 a.) in Layer Breton owned by Edward Morley, uncle to the wife of P. B. Scalé, surveyor extraordinary. The cartouche of this map is similar to that of the Yeldham survey, both being neatly executed in the classical style of the time. Dyer's concentration on houses and lack of any survey of even one whole farm is most odd if he was a full-time land surveyor.

In 1756 JOHN BLYTH, "Junior, of Colchester", advertised that he and Joseph Bird of Ipswich "have set up together at land surveying".[112] There is no other record[113] of Bird but, also in 1756, J. Blyth Jnr mapped[114] a small fen in Colchester. The map has a pleasing cartouche in the style of the time but under the scale bar is a pendant decoration exactly similar to that which became the trade mark of all the maps by William Cole of Colchester. There is a long time gap before Blyth's next surviving maps. In 1775 he made two maps for James Round, each of a small farm (one[115] in Copford, the other[116] in Stanway). Neither of these maps has the pendant decoration below the scale bar. However, in 1781 Blyth surveyed[117] with William Cole another farm for the Round family and this map does have the pendant decoration. It is also the last map of Blyth's, and Cole was later to do many surveys for the Round family.

At that time there were a number of Blyths in the Colchester area, including an attorney, farmers in Langham and a John Blyth who held several parish offices in Boxted from 1763 to 1798.

Before coming to the leading north Essex surveyor, one name has to be taken out from any roll of land surveyors. A survey of a farm in Birch, owned by William Round, is dated 1750. The map[118] states clearly "Drawn by Robert Simms". There is no evidence to consider Simms as a surveyor, and as a draftsman he was second rate.

JOHN STORER had a long and busy career, eventually doing all the jobs that became the mark of the chartered surveyor. He is probably the best example of the times of an Essex surveyor working for Essex land owners. His few excursions outside Essex were on their behalf. His working life was spent in Halstead, where in 1768 he married Mary Gibling also of that town. Curiously it was only on a few maps dated 1781–3 that he put "John Storer of Halstead".

Storer's first known work is a map[119] drawn by him in 1765 from a survey made in 1689 by William Kendall of a farm in Great Waltham belonging to Mr Whaley of Colchester. The map does not copy Kendall's style of cartography, apart from the drawing of an "irritated eagle" in one corner. A clumsily drawn female figure sits on either side of the map, one clutching a sheaf of corn, the other holding a sickle as if it were a mirror. The plain scale bar has a rounded end and above it is a divider lying on its side. All this is remarkably reminiscent of Timothy Skynner's inexplicably poor work in 1731–3.

A year later Storer managed a neat map with a good clear script for his survey[120] of a farm (285 a.) in Colne Engayne[121]. As time went on his cartography continued to improve, particularly in his scripts, which followed the fashion to a clear print-like appearance. His rather dull cartouches remained in the mid-century idiom. However he made useful maps that showed land usage and land holding in terms of free- or copyhold.

In 1768 Storer was employed by the Dean and Chapter of St Pauls to survey[122] their 600 acre estate in Wickham St Pauls, previously surveyed for them by John Coffyn of Great Burstead. It is interesting that they used a London surveyor, Samuel Warner, to measure their Barling estate in 1766.

Storer mainly worked for big land owners whose estates were conveniently near to Halstead. He seems to have taken over from Timothy Skynner, who died in 1770, as a major Essex surveyor. The Honeywood family had employed Skynner, particularly for the 1764 survey of Markshalls, their large home estate. Storer was called in for the outlying lands, mapping[123] a farm in White Colne in 1769 and[124] in Kirby-le-Soken in 1775. Subsequently the Honeywood estate book[125] indicates that Storer was surveying lands in Bocking and Finchingfield in the 1780s, and in 1795 Storer mapped[126] a small farm in Feering for Filmer Honeywood. The written list[126] of lands in Totham dated 1796 and the undated anonymous maps[128] of four of the farms listed, all belonging to Filmer Honeywood, may well have been taken from Storer's surveys. In short he appears to have been the "on call" land surveyor for the Honeywoods throughout his career.

For Lord Nugent of Gosfield Park Storer worked as surveyor and also agent for the estate. He surveyed[129] the 3000 acre Gosfield estate in 1772 and two years later started to make "the agreements for Lord Nugent's farms belonging to his Gosfield estates".[130] In 1791 he produced a book of nine maps[131] to show the copy- and freehold lands of the manors of Gosfield, Bell House and Shardloes, all Nugent land. So it is very probable that he was concerned with the 1793 field book[132] and with the accompanying boundary alterations that were put on his 1772 map of Gosfield.

Du Cane of Braxted employed Storer to survey his lands in Tollesbury. The Du Cane accounts[133] record "To John Storer 18 November 1774 the sum of £24-4-0 for measuring and mapping my farms in Tollesbury . . . and for measuring some copyhold estates in the manor of Tollesbury." The known maps of this work are of Tollesbury Hall[134] (1773; 725 a.) and five maps,[135] all dated 1774, bound in a book and showing holdings of 19 to 90 acres. It is interesting that the last two maps in this book are dated 1778 and by Matthew Hall of Maldon. Why was Storer not commissioned to finish the Tollesbury survey?

Storer's map of Tollesbury Hall has an attractive cartouche looking like pink crumpled ribbon or even shredded lettuce. This pink style of decoration was used by Storer for his additions to John Rocque's Ongar map for Earl Tylney when he "viewed" the farm in 1776. The best documented relationship between Storer and his clients was that with Sir Thomas Spencer-Wilson of Sussex, who gained his Essex estates in 1767 by marriage to Jane Weller. For him Storer produced a series of maps,[136] of farms in Little Laver (1781; 360 a.), Hatfield Broadoak (1782; 153 a.), Great Canfield (1784; 400 a.) and a sketch map of a 48 acre farm in White Roothing (1784). A series of letters[137] from Storer to Spencer-Wilson (from 1781 onwards) shows that Storer was land agent and general surveyor of these estates, valuing farms and buildings, arranging the sale of timber and supervising the repairs of barns and houses. In addition he travelled to Spencer-Wilson's small land holdings in Suffolk and Cambridgeshire, reporting and measuring. All his letters were written in good "copper-plate" script and one contains a neat plan of a small Cambridgeshire property.

Storer had a life-long commitment to the Honeywood, Nugent and Spencer-Wilson estates but he also surveyed for others. He mapped farms in Earls Colne[138] (1783), Colne Engayne[139] and Black Notley[140] (both in 1790), and Belchamp Otten[141] (1793). For Saville of Bocking he mapped in Belchamp Walter[142] (1789) and Pebmarsh[143] (1796). His one trip to Suffolk was to survey for a Brantham land owner[144] (1788).

Like many other land surveyors, Storer turned his attention to the sale of land, first advertising[145] land for sale in 1783 and continuing to do so up to 1799. He extended these interests by going into partnership in 1790 with an auctioneer of Halstead, Mr Oakley. But this lasted only until September 1791, when he changed the partnership to another Halstead auctioneer, Mr Woolman. Both of them were agents for the Phoenix Fire Assurance and were able to offer mortgages: "Upon land security only, any sum from one to three thousand pounds may be had by applying to Mr Storer, Halstead, auctioneer, land and timber surveyor."

It had become fashionable towards the end of the 18th century for local land owners to defend their property by forming an association for the prosecution of felons. Storer became the secretary to the Halstead association. It was an obvious way of keeping in with his clients, and some other successful Essex surveyors held such a post in their local association.

John Storer's career was one of variety and success. In the mid-1790s the first publication of the *Universal British Directory* listed only two Essex land surveyors; one was Storer and the other William Cole of Colchester.

Storer made his will[146] when "infirm of body" on 5 October 1803 and left an annual income to his wife Mary, his house to his elder son John and some property to his younger son Roger. As there is a tenuous link of mensuration between land surveying and excise work (John Woodward, excise officer of Bocking, made a good map of Essex in 1799) it is interesting that both John and Roger Storer were excise men. John was in Rayleigh in 1785–7 living on land owned by the Excise,[147] and the Board of Excise in 1799 " . . . ordered that John Storer of Halstead, 1st Divn. Essex Colln., be made an examiner".[148] Roger Storer was clerk to the Collector of Excise in Colchester.

Cartouche by William Moore (see p. 122), 1779. The drapery and tree design is a crude plagiarism from the cartouche on Chapman and André's map of Essex, published two years before.

CENTRAL ESSEX

O OF THE LOCAL surveyors who were working before 1739 only John Lee of Baddow continued a busy career in the locality during the earlier years of this time period.
MATTHEW DAYLES was, like Agnis of Colchester, a yeoman farmer and an occasional land surveyor. The 1734 Freeholder's Book lists him as resident in Rettenden, aged 30 years. On his 1746 map he described himself as "of Buttsbury" and his will,[149] proved in 1764, described him as a yeoman of that parish. He also held land in North Benfleet and Wickford, all bequeathed to his widow.

Dayles' first map[150] (1739) is "a draught" of two Mayland farms, one surveyed by himself, the other drawn from a survey by William Cole (of Ramsden) in 1720. The remarkable feature of this map is the border decoration of large coloured separate flowers, so exactly like those of Fallowes that Dayles must have copied them from a Fallowes' map. The two lived fairly close to one another and Dayles' second map[151] (1743) is of one farm in Purleigh, the parish in which Fallowes died. However Dayles did not repeat a floral design on this or his third map[152] (1746) which showed a small farm in Prittlewell. The cartouches of the three maps go from a slight frond and flower pattern through a well drawn mantle to frame the title and on to a pleasant light classical "framework". His scripts are neat with a sloped cursive hand. The slender evidence of his work suggests a man helping out his fellow farmers with small surveys close to his home.

His two Essex maps show JOSIAH FINLEY to have been of Billericay in 1747 when working in nearby Ramsden Bellhouse and later (c. 1760) of Chelmsford when working equally close to home in Little Waltham. Both maps are intriguing. The 1747 one[153] shows land (133 a.) in Ramsden belonging to Jeremiah Bentham of Barking, a lawyer much given to dabbling in property and the father of the political philosopher Jeremy Bentham (1748–1832). The only other known map for Bentham is an anonymous one,[154] dated 1744, of a farm in Harlow. It is not in Finley's style. Finley's map is well laid out and has good decorative scripts with a slight classical cartouche and plain tables of explanation and contents. On its right side there is a square blank space, ruled off in black line, which has signs of something having been pasted on to it. The addition must have been some decorative panel, perhaps a view of a house, probably made by someone other than Finley.

The second map[155] is undated. Like the first, its title starts "An accurate survey of . . ." but Finley puts "Delint." after his name, thus casting doubt on his being the surveyor. The map is catalogued as *c.* 1750 but it contains a comment, apparently in Finley's hand, on a field bought in 1761. The cartouche is a brightly coloured design incorporating a basket of flowers at the top and a grotesque face at the bottom, the whole being very pleasing. The map was made for John Judd who owned five separate farms in Little Waltham.[156] Finley shows only one on his map but it is possible that he surveyed the others. There is a curious sketch map[157] of two of Judd's farms on which is written "John Judd Jnr. copied this map 1788." Maybe the original was by Finley.

A tailpiece without comment. A map[158] of a small estate in Shimpling, Suffolk, made in 1765 is signed simply "Finley".

Only one schoolmaster figures in this account. THOMAS GROUT surveyed and mapped[154] in 1748 a 228 acre farm in Beauchamp Roding. The title is displayed on a well drawn mantle, and Grout adds to his name "Schoolmaster of Fyfield". Presumably he was employed in the school founded in 1687 by the rector of Fyfield, Anthony Walker, for poor children to be taught reading, writing and arithmetic. This would make Grout the very pattern of Oliver Goldsmith's village schoolmaster. In line with this is the will[160] of a husbandman of Moreton (next to Fyfield) signed by T. Grout; a service to the local community often undertaken by schoolmasters.

JOSEPH GRIMSEY is known only from one map[161] (1748) of a farm in Writtle. It is a neat undistinguished map bearing the arms of Comyns, who owned the farm.

JOSEPH DAWSON was very much a local surveyor, his area of work being confined to a narrow band from the Easters to Danbury. His 24-year career is probably not fully represented by his surviving maps as there are blank years from 1764 to 1771 and from 1775 to his last map in 1787. Some of the blanks can be filled in by his written surveys. He seems to have had a long association with Richard Hoare of Boreham, measuring for him a wood in Boreham in 1758, some pasture there in 1767 and more woodland in 1776. For the last survey he was paid at the going rate of sixpence an acre. The survey and payment was ordered by Hoare's agent, Mr Hurrell, who features as a surveyor in 1798.

Of Dawson's 16 mapped surveys, 11 are of areas less than 200 acres and four are of parsonage (or parish charity) land. His furthest expedition was to Radwinter for the Wolfe family, who had commissioned his first survey in Good Easter. His largest survey was for Lord Waltham, who was an Olmius, neighbours to Hoare. One of Dawson's maps was only a sketch copy[163] (1762) of Little Baddow Common; maybe the original was by John Lee.

Illustration, page 62 As might be expected from an unpretentious local surveyor, perhaps living near Chelmsford, Dawson's cartography is neat, explicit but not individualistic. His style remained unchanged throughout his career. Buildings were shown in perspective, cartouches were of a classical "framework" design and the scale bars had simple decorations. The whole flavour is of a somewhat outdated style.

Maps by TIMOTHY SKYNNER are dated from 1713 to 1767, a length of career strongly suggesting a father to son succession rather than one Timothy Skynner. Supporting the father and son idea is the entry in the 1768 Freeholder's Book that gives Skynner's age as 40 years; this man died in 1770. Dr Emmison has pointed out on grounds of differing style that the Skynner of the early maps is not the one who mapped from 1746 onwards, although some

TABLE SEVEN

THE MAPS OF JOSEPH DAWSON

Date	Parish	Comment	Reference
1754	Good Easter	105 a. farm for Wolfe	D/DTu 237
1756	Broomfield	95 a. parsonage land	D/DQ 11/114
"	Radwinter	316 a. for Wolfe	D/DQ 5
"	Danbury	108 a. farm for ? Fytche	D/DMa P8
1758	Danbury	280 a. Danbury Place for Fytche	D/DMa P8
"	Lt. Waltham	130 a. parish charity	D/P 220/25/117
1759	High Easter	200a. parsonage land (Tufnell)	T/M 269
"	Good Easter	56 a. draft map for Clerk of Baddow	D/DSp P2
1760	Widford	Farm	MS dept. Br. Lib.
1761	Lt. Waltham	Part of Pratts Farm (in notebook)	D/DU 738 (A.7844)
1761	Margaret Roothing	58 a. parsonage land	D/P 309/3/1
1762	Baddow	Copy of old map of Common	D/DRa P11
1764	Finchingfield	178 a. farm for Ruggles	T/M 31
1771	Broomfield	487 a. Broomfield Hall (Ld. Waltham)	D/DHt P15
1774	Mashbury	74 a. farm	D/DU 77/41
1775	Grt Waltham	60 a. farm	D/DTu 202
1787	Grt Leighs	95 a. farm	D/DBw P1

similarities would suggest a father and son relationship. The identity of signatures on bills shows that the Skynner of 1746 who was the one who died in 1770. Details of maps and clients indicate that the man of 1746 was drawing his own maps by 1744. Although the evidence indicates two Timothy Skynners, the cartographic history is presented as the work of one man, because it is not possible to separate the two with certainty.

Only three known Skynner maps cover the years 1713–28. The first was made for a Thaxted Quaker, but there is no record of Skynner being a Quaker. The most decorated map is of Peldon (1728). The scale bar has squared ends, later bars have curved ends. The divider above has curved cross-blades, later dividers are drawn with straight blades. The cartouche has much colour, some little flowers and two badly drawn cherubs. The polar indicator is a star shape, unlike the later compass roses with a finely painted central flower. One interesting point is that the hedgerow trees are shown with a distinction made between a full tree and a pollard.

Skynner's career as a full-time land measurer took off with his major Coggeshall surveys for Du Cane. So much of his work concerns Coggeshall and neighbouring parishes that Skynner most likely lived there. An advertisement[164] of 1741 is quoted as naming Skynner "Land Surveyor of Coggeshall". But his name does not appear in the parish registers or in the well kept lists of ratepayers; nor does he feature on the list of Du Cane's tenants.

His maps of Coggeshall, 1731 and 1732, have a well drawn "working surface" but bizarre badly executed decorations. The titles of both are displayed on a banner, which in the 1731 map is held by curious cherubs. Very odd human figures are there, a female holding a spade and a man with an amazing headdress holding a large sort of horn. The 1732 map shows a seated woman touching a terrestrial globe, a badly drawn figure that Skynner included on his 1733 Coggeshall map from a survey "as taken in 1720 and redrawn 1733 by T. Skynner". The one good feature of these maps is the delicate compass rose.

Skynner's 1733 survey of East Donyland covered the whole parish. This estate had been bought in 1730 by David Gansell of Leyton who commissioned the survey. That Gansell came from Leyton may explain Skynner's trip to that parish in 1734 to survey only 52 acres for a local resident. This expedition could have included some work for Gansell on his Leyton estate.

The title of the 1735 map of Du Cane farms states "as measured by Mr James Gould in 1721 and redrawn by Tim Skynner". Gould's map still exists and it can be seen that Skynner in his own style produced a copy on a reduced scale. A year before this copy was made the timber on these farms was measured[165] by Francis Flatt of Peckham, Surrey, taking the description of each field from Gould's map. The point is that Skynner was not asked to survey the timber, a job that was the stock in trade for many land surveyors. Indeed Skynner's maps do not dwell on timber as did those of Nicholls.

The 1741 map of Easthope Hall, Coggeshall, is typical of Skynner's style at that time. The cartouche is a simple broad "frame", the compass rose well drawn in colour and the scale bar with rounded ends having a good divider above. The original map is in the Public Record Office, and there for an intriguing reason. Easthope Hall had belonged to Thomas Green, who died without issue in 1726, leaving the estate to three co-heirs. One of them was John Blandford, who in 1714 was convicted and attainted of felony of robbery on the highway. One third of the estate was therefore escheated to the Crown. George Baker, named on the map as owner of the estate, petitioned the Crown for a lease of the escheated third in the year that Skynner made his survey. The Crown eventually granted the lease in 1745 but kept the map, which owes its preservation to highway robbery.[166]

The year 1741 also saw a great military camp set up at Lexden, Colchester. One of the three generals in charge was Honeywood, for whom Skynner had made extensive surveys in 1736. Skynner published an engraved plan of this camp, presumably from his original drawings. The plan was published by him in London, made by J. Tinney and engraved by M. Gravelot. The present scarcity of copies[167] suggests that the plan was not a best seller, although noted by Gough.

If there were two Skynners, then the likely last job of the father was to accompany Du Cane on the 1743 perambulation of the parish bounds of Coggeshall. It was not unusual for the man who had surveyed a parish to return and walk the bounds. This perambulation is recorded[168] in writing and a note of it added to Skynner's 1731 map of the parish.

There is a three year gap between 1741 and further Skynner maps made in 1744. In these the style and script has changed, the cartouches becoming initially an uncomplicated rococo design. The 1744 maps were made for Morden College, Kent, whose several properties in Coggeshall are shown in six maps. The seventh map shows a small property in Purfleet and includes a "view of the town of Colchester" showing the skyline.

A second institutional survey came from this work. Public bodies usually minuted the discussion that preceded a survey and so provided a hint of what must have been conversations between private land owners and their agents before calling in a land surveyor. In this instance it was the Commissioners for Sewers for the East Greenwich Levels.[169] In March 1743 they reviewed their available maps and records, observing "with regret that all the ancient surveys and records of the court are lost and that the only map we have of the Level is that of 1697". They also noted that "a great inconvenience attending the plan of the old map and which rendered it almost useless was the variety of marks used on each piece of land so that when the book was lost the plan was useless". The modern archivist feels just the same when faced with a map divorced from its field book. The Commissioners had an answer to this problem by insisting that any new map should "have inserted a table at the bottom of the map" so that the map itself would be a sufficient record.

After lengthy deliberations the Commissioners ordered a new map " . . . by Mr Skynner who was recommended to them as a skilfull surveyor". The recommendation very probably came from Morden College, who were major land holders in the Level and whose representative was in charge of the Commissioner's expenditure in 1746. Skynner produced a draft map of the Level in April 1745 and the completed map appeared later in the year. He duly appended below the map a complete table of contents. Quite out of the Skynner style was his border decoration of brightly coloured flowers. The Commissioners checked Skynner's work by getting a Mr Grimett to survey an 18 acre sample. His measurement was the same as Skynner's and the Commissioners were pleased. "We have full proof of the skill and exactness of the surveyor, if he has been equally careful in all the other pieces (and we have reason to believe he has)". The map was finally declared the official survey in 1746, when Skynner was asked to provide a copy, which he delivered in 1747. It was obviously a good survey as it was used as the basis for an updated survey of 1834.

The rest of Skynner's work was for private land owners. One of his two Thaxted maps of 1746 for a parish charity has a bill for it. Skynner charged sixpence an acre for his survey, 6s 6d for the vellum and eleven shillings for his assistant. His signature on this bill is identical to that on a bill of 1762. His next major survey was for Charles Smith of Hill Hall, Theydon. In 1749 Skynner made eight maps of Smith's lands in Thaxted and five maps of his Theydon estate. In 1752 he journeyed north to Norfolk to make one survey.

The year 1755 was important for Skynner. He surveyed the whole parishes of Great Bardfield and Bardfield Saling for Jones Raymond.[170] This work is likely to have been commissioned by Raymond's agent John Yeldham, also agent to Lewis Way, for whom Skynner had surveyed in 1749. In November of that year Skynner moved to Moulsham, Chelmsford, to stay there until his death. One of his first clients after the move was Du Cane who had himself moved from Coggeshall to Braxted in 1751. A new client was Mildmay of Moulsham (Skynner was a juror at Mildmay's manorial court of April 1763). Many items of survey for Mildmay are detailed in Skynner's account[171] rendered in 1762; of these only one is recorded on a map (the vellum for which was charged by Skynner at 7s 6d). This is a clear indication that land surveyors earned a lot of their keep by measuring and inspecting land without mapping. Skynner, whose maps show so little interest in timber, wrote to Mildmay[172] on 8 January 1757 to say that measurement of the woods "would admit of 17 acres to be felled at 18 years growth", but added "As its full late to fell a great quantity this year, if the Woodman was immediately to begin to fell in a workmanlike manner what he could clear by the beginning of June observing to leave all things likely to become timber and an exact account in writing kept of all expenses and outgoings attending such felling and carrying out you would thereby come at a true knowledge of the value per acre of the whole wood." The English may be involved but the advice is clear and typical of what a land surveyor was asked to proffer.

Skynner's 1758 map of the Mildmay estates in Danbury and Sandon can also be seen in its initial rough working drawing.[173] On the back of the paper used for this are incomplete workings labelled "The reduced estate of St. Thomas' Hospital at Parndon, 1759." A fair copy of this reduction is not known but the agent for the hospital's Parndon estates was none other than John Yeldham, who made a written survey of them in 1774 (the existing estate maps date back to the 17th century). The Mildmay connection is further emphasized by Skynner surveying a small parcel of land in Chelmsford for the attorney Thomas Pocklington, who was Mildmay's steward. Later (1764) when Skynner started to advertise land for sale, some advertisements included Pocklington.

Skynner's career after his move to Moulsham was certainly not confined to working with Mildmay. Lord Maynard claimed his services, first with an engraved dull picture[174] of Easton Lodge (1756) and then with a very major expedition to survey his extensive lands in Suffolk.

This entailed the making, in 1757, of 20 maps to cover the scattered estate. In 1759 Skynner surveyed Maynard's huge Ashdon, Essex, estate but managed to get it all on to one large map. It must be remembered that the Easton Lodge estate had been surveyed by Laurence in 1730, so Skynner could not do more than make his picture of Easton Lodge and its park.

Apart from his 1757 travels in Suffolk, Skynner went up to Bedfordshire to survey the estate inherited by Richard Ray in that year. While he was there Skynner negotiated with the Turnpike Trust as to the best route for the road that crossed Ray's boundaries. "I walked with the Chief Surveyor and set forth to him I thought if the road were carried thro' sixteen acres it would be . . . a vast deal less expense to the Commissioners."[175] He drew a plan to show Ray what he had suggested. Ray called him back for further surveying in 1765, also a year in which Skynner went to Suffolk, this time for a single small survey.

Another client to recall Skynner was Jones Raymond who had him surveying his Coggeshall and Kelvedon estates in 1758. For some inexplicable reason Raymond brought in Fairchild from way out of Essex in 1760 to survey his Shalford estate. Skynner must have thought that he should have been asked, unless there had been a row about his previous work.

For John Hennicker of Stratford House, East Ham, Skynner surveyed his Dunmow estate in 1759 and then, in 1764, made his second journey to Thames-side Essex to survey the East Ham estate.

As with the Mildmays, Skynner had a long association with the Strutts of Terling. He made a series of maps of their lands in Terling (mainly) the Easters and Woodham Ferrers. Of the 14 maps seven were from Skynner's own surveys; four of these are dated 1760, two in 1764 (the map of a small farm in High Easter dated that year may well be part of the series but escaped the family archive) and one in 1766. Two other Skynner surveys are undated but the properties were bought by Strutt in 1762 and 1764. The seven maps made by Skynner from other people's surveys are all undated. One, of 31 acres in Woodham Ferrers, was surveyed by John Lee in 1756. This was the last work by Lee and it is interesting that Skynner's move to Moulsham had not by then attracted Strutt's attention. The other properties surveyed previously had been in the Strutt family for many years. The surveyors were Ralph Dowcett (a 17th century man), Robert Chapman, John Madison and two Essex men, William Pullen and Jeremiah Nicholls.

The Honeywood connection of the 1730s was renewed by Skynner in 1764, notably with the survey of Markshalls, the Honeywood's home estate. But after that Skynner's career was drawing to an end, perhaps with failing physical powers, as Honeywood started to employ John Storer as a surveyor in 1769.

Skynner's last map, 1767, was signed just "T.S." He had used his initials only on his 1765 map for James Round, but otherwise the rule was "T. Skynner", occasionally in the earlier years using "Tim°" instead of the T. His style from 1746 onwards progressed with the times. He drew in black ink very fine detailed rococo cartouches, the sort of design that can be found surrounding many printed items of the mid-18th century. His compass roses were always elegant and well coloured, often with long rays spreading from them to cover blank spaces on his maps. The rounded ends of his checker-board scale bars were also a feature. He produced very fine maps that were informative and pleasing.

Rococo cartouche by George Hutson Jnr. (see p. 125), 1777 (see also illus. p. 6).

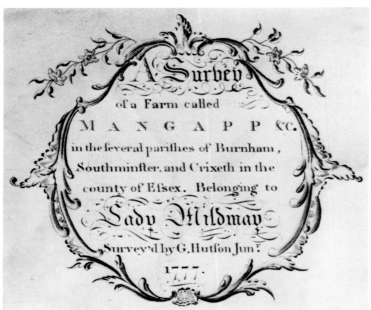

When he died in 1770, Robert Dallinger, schoolmaster of Witham, who hoped to succeed him, called him "The late eminent surveyor in the county of Essex". Certainly Skynner was the perfect example of a land measurer. Although towards the end of his career he was concerned with land sales, these other surveyor's activities played a small part in his work. He was employed consistently by some of the major Essex land owners, and the large number of his surviving maps may in part be attributable to these land owners being the sort of people whose archives were most likely to come to county record offices. His career also shows that land measurement was not the most profitable occupation. The parish rate records show that Skynner's Moulsham property was valued at only five pounds per annum. His will,[176] proved in March 1771, showed that the property had been bought with a mortgage lent by his friend James Wyatt of Little Canfield Hall. There is no mention of a wife or family. Wyatt inherited the property to sell as soon as convenient and at the best price. Skynner's servant, Mary Sadler, received £20. There is no mention of Skynner in the Moulsham parish burial records so he disappeared quietly, only to be known for his splendid maps.

TABLE EIGHT

THE MAPS OF TIMOTHY SKYNNER

Date	Parish	Comment	Reference	
1713	Stebbing	61 a. for J. Hills, Thaxted Quaker	D/DHt P39	
1717	Langford	20 a. wood	D/DU 261/9	
1728	Peldon	86 a. for Mrs Thurstan of Suffolk	D/DHt P3	
1731	Coggeshall	Whole manor of Grt Coggeshall for Du Cane	D/DU 19/2	
1732	" "	171 a. manor of Lt. Coggeshall for Du Cane	D/DU 19/15	
1733	" "	69 a. "Taken 1720", redrawn by Skynner	D/DMa P3	
"	Barnston	162 a. for Lukin	D/DK P5	
"	E. Donyland	Whole parish for Ganzell	D/DU 315	
1734	Leyton	52 a. for Wakelin of Leyton	In private hands	
1735	Coggeshall	642 a. drawn from Gould's 1721 survey for Du Cane	D/DU 19/4	
1736	Bocking	166 a. for Honeywood	D/DHh P3	
"	Felsted	104 a. for Honeywood	D/DHt P7	
"	Hanningfield etc.	200 a. for Honeywood	D/DCm P1	
"	Bardfield	41 a. for Gladwin ?of Coggeshall	D/DTa P1	
"	Lexden	17 a. only	D/DPa P1	
1740	Norton Mandeville	Whole parish for Elderton of London	D/DCc P1	*Illustration, frontispiece*
1741	Coggeshall	230 a. for G. Baker	T/M 178 & original in PRO	
"	Wethersfield	Whole parish for J. Clerk	D/DFy P1	
1744	Coggeshall	Six maps of lands of Morden College Kent, and one map of Purfleet mill	T/M 301	
1745	*Kent* (Greenwich)	Marshes for Comms. of Sewers	GLC Record Office	
1746	Thaxted	Two maps (285 a.) for parish charity	D/P 16/25/68 & 94a	
"	" "	52 a. farm	D/DK P7	
"	Hatfield Broadoak	110 a. farm for W. Round	D/DU 737/2	
1749	Dunmow	177 a. for Lewis Way	D/DU 234/82	
"	Thaxted & Theydon	Estates of Charles Smith 8 maps Thaxted, 5 maps Theydon	D/DSh P3	
1750	Fingringhoe	138 a. farm	D/DEl P75	
1752	Witham	300 a. for Rev. Pettiward	T/M 35	
"	*Norfolk*	map noted by Dr Eden		
1754	Colchester & Wivenhoe	43 a. & 41 a. on one map	D/DR P10	
"	Wethersfield	48 a. only of farm (anonymous)	D/DGh T19	
1755	Bardfield	Whole parishes of Grt B. & B. Saling for Jones Raymond	T/M 253	
"	Shopland	179 a. for Tyrrell	D/DU 628	
"	Grt Braxted	96 a. for Du Cane	D/DDc P6	
1756	Chelmsford	169 a. for Mildmay	D/DM P7	
1757	" "	33 a. for Pocklington	D/DDw P52	
"	High Easter	220 a. of farm	D/DK P9	
"	*Suffolk*	20 maps of Lord Maynard's scattered estates	Suffolk RO	
"	*Bedfordshire*	Manor at Colmworth for R. Ray	Beds. RO	
1758	Coggeshall & Kelvedon	2500 a. on one map of Jones Raymond's estates	T/M 230 & D/DMb P18	
"	Danbury	305 a. for Mildmay	D/DM P7a	

1759	Dunmow	175 a. for J. Henniker	T/M 15
"	Ashden	Lord Maynard's 9732 a. estate on one map	Private hands
1760	Terling	155 a. for Strutt	T/M 65/4
"	" "	147 a. for Strutt (undated)	T/M 65/2
1762	Dunmow	only 11 a.	D/DU 293/152
"	Witham	132 a. of glebe land	D/P 30
1763	Terling	64 a. for Strutt	T/M 65/13
1764	Good Easter	117 a. for Strutt	T/M 65/11
"	High Easter	118 a. for Strutt	T/M 65/11
"	" "	31 a. ? for Strutt	D/DU 111
"	East Ham	385 a. for J. Henniker (of E. Ham)	T/M 18
"	Markshall	1429 a. for Honeywood (on one map)	D/DCm P14
"	Feering	326 a. for Honeywood	D/DHt P11
1765	East Mersea	130 a. for Jas. Round	D/DC 39/4
"	Wakering	193 a. for Tyrrell	D/DGe P13
"	Writtle etc.	92 a. scattered holdings for Strutt	T/M 65/5
"	*Suffolk*	Thornham Hall	Suffolk RO
"	*Bedfordshire*	Part of J. Ray's estate	Beds. RO
1766	Copford	521 a. for Rev. J. Harrison	D/DEl P9
"	Woodham Ferrers	53 a. for Strutt	T/M 65/9
1767	High Laver	High Laver Hall (377 a.) signed "T.S."	D/DEs T88
(1763–6)	(seven maps for Strutt from others' surveys in Terling, and Woodham Ferrers)		T/M 65/1, 3, 6 8, 10, 12, 14

Illustration, page 13 [East Ham]

SOUTH ESSEX

IN THIS TIME period Brentwood features as the locality for a diverse collection of land surveyors, mainly with another occupation.

GEORGE SANGSTER is ill-represented by the handful of his surviving maps. His primary occupation, like that of Samuel Driver in the Old Kent Road, was running a nursery garden where "All the gentlemen, ladies and others, lovers of that most rational amusement of planting and gardening" could buy a wide variety of plants, shrubs and trees.[177] The 18th century use of the word "rational" is to be relished.

As Sangster's first known map (1755) is of a whole manor, made for John Porter, an alderman of the City of London, it may well be that his career as a surveyor had started before that date. The second map, an even larger survey, was commissioned by the esoteric Society for the Propagation of the Gospel in New England and made in 1766. However a lot must have happened between 1755 and 1766 as Sangster advertised his move to a new nursery garden in 1767, adding that he was continuing "to survey, map and value, buy and sell estates woods and timbers as usual". In short, a full scale operation as land surveyor and estate agent was already in being. His first advertisement of land to sell was published in 1767.

The new nursery garden that Sangster had purchased was a seven acre property known as Little Birds at Brook Hill, Brentwood. It was described as "all that dwelling house, sheds, yards and nursery ground situate on the south side of Brook Street, abutting north thereon, south and west on Prittle farm and east on Upper Birds".[178]

The small Lambourne map is not by Sangster but drawn anonymously from his survey of 3 Feb. 1767. The map was probably made for a dispute in ownership as it lists "the woods in question" with the owners' names. The next map in Sangster's hand is dated 1769 and shows a Chigwell farm "belonging to the Grammar School of Anthony Brown, Sergt. at Law, Brentwood".[179] The decoration of this map is of great interest. To go back to the beginning, Sangster's 1755 map has an apology for a plain "frame" cartouche. His 1766 map shows a new lyrical style which is copied and refined in the 1769 map. The cartouche has a light frame wrapped in leaves and, on either side, a beautifully painted peach sliced to show the stone. The date of survey and Hutson's name are surrounded by an oval leaf chain with four delicately coloured flowers. The table of contents is framed by classical pillars; on top of each

Illustration, page 54

Illustration, page 95

Detail showing the quayside at Mistley from a volume of maps prepared by Peter Bernard Scalé (see p. 123), for Richard Rigby in 1778.

A map of Mistley Hall, seat of Richard Rigby, from the same volume. Note the agricultural motifs around the polar indicator and Scalé's characteristic "torn paper" cartouche incorporating a view from the R. Stour.

there is an elderly cherub face with wings at the neck. The 1769 version has cherubs with heavy eyebrows. Compared with an oblong scale bar in 1755, both the 1766 and 1769 maps have a "stepped" scale bar, narrowing towards the centre. The remarkable thing is that the style of Sangster's 1769 map was faithfully copied by George Hutson (of Rayleigh, then of Hutton) on his first map of 1772. It is so close a copy that Hutson must have had Sangster's map before him as he drew. What is more, the "stepped" scale bar was to become Hutson's trademark on all his maps and, in due course, was adopted by Robert Baker of Witham (and of Writtle).

Unfortunately there is a gap of 14 years before Sangster's next surviving map of 1785. By this time his style had changed with the times. He went back to an oblong scale bar, his cartouche was a simple leaf chain design and his contents tables just boxed in by a line. His rather awkward script had become more pleasing. In 1787 he surveyed by himself in Suffolk (his only expedition away from the Brentwood area) but with his son in South Weald. The last two maps for Neave of Dagnams, near Brentwood, are undistinguished. He never managed to repeat the artistry of 1766 and 1769 and his son took no further interest in the business, although both were advertising land for sale in the 1780s. Sangster senior had been selling property from the time that he set up as a surveyor. He was an enterprising businessman, at one time selling deer "of beautiful colours and proper ages for succession", and auctioning wine as well as land. In 1794, "being now inclined to retire from business", he put up his nursery garden for sale, his son being unable or unwilling to carry it on.

TABLE NINE

KNOWN MAPS OF GEORGE SANGSTER

Date	Parish	Comment	Reference
1755	Springfield	Manor of Barnes, 397 a.	D/DMa P5
1766	Tolleshunt	Beckenham Hall, 425 a.	Guildhall Library
1767	Lambourne	Survey only, 40 a.	D/DQ 41/4
1769	Chigwell	Farm, 129 a.	D/DBg 70/2
1785	W. Hanningfield	Farm, 105 a.	D/DGe P21
1787	*Suffolk* (Westhall)	Farm, 86 a.	Suffolk RO
"	S. Weald	Farm, 112 a. (& Son)	D/DTw P5
1790	Eastwood	Two maps of farms (117 a. + 74 a.)	D/DNe P4 & 5

ISAAC TAYLOR made four Essex estate maps, all in 1755, and on all he put "of Brentwood". The maps showed farms owned by small land owners in Hockley[180] (43 a.), Eastwood[181] (110 a.), Rayleigh[182] (118 a.) and away in Steeple Bumstead[183] (255 a.) This last map has no cartouche but the others have pleasing cartouches, painted, not drawn. Two have the title enclosed by romantic trees, a miniature sylvan scene that became popular with cartographers in the 1770s. Taylor's scripts show versatile and skilled penmanship. He also, in 1756, surveyed and mapped[184] a 180 acre farm in Flamstead, Hertfordshire, again adding "of Brentwood" after his name. The cartouche of this map is of a more formal floral design but he enclosed some written notes with a mantle held by cherubs.

Thanks to the prominence of his son, the Rev. Isaac Taylor, as a nonconformist clergyman who in turn fathered a literate family, the Taylor story is well documented in biographies old and new.[185] Isaac Taylor, the land surveyor, was born in Worcester in 1730, the son of William, a brass founder and engraver. Having learnt his trade from his father, Isaac sought wider horizons and so walked to London in 1752. There he was employed by a cutler, Josiah Jeffries, who lived in Brentwood and was the brother of Thomas Jeffries the well known cartographer. Isaac did the right thing by marrying the boss's daughter Sarah at Shenfield in May, 1754. There followed a brief interlude of land surveying before his return to a London career as an engraver in 1757. There is another Isaac Taylor map[186] of a Hertfordshire farm which is dated 1758 and does not add "of Brentwood"; the style is similar to his 1756 map.

Isaac must have kept up his Brentwood home, as his sons, Charles (born 1756) and Isaac (born 1759), both went to Brentwood school.

Charles Taylor became a London engraver and Isaac entered the church, later being in Lavenham and finally in Colchester. The Rev. Isaac also had a son named Isaac who became an engraver but this time concerned with engraving maps. In particular there is a map[187] of the road from Woodbridge to Debenham (Suffolk) made by Isaac Johnson in 1800 and engraved by Isaac Taylor Jnr. of Colchester. It could be called a full circle from the original Isaac Taylor's brief career as a land surveyor round to his grandson's engraving a map by a land surveyor who also worked in Essex.

As if there were not already enough Isaac Taylors in the 18th century there is further confusion with the cartographer and land surveyor, Isaac Taylor of Ross, Herefordshire. Unfortunately his career started in 1754 but it continued to flourish in to the late 1770s. Apart from many estate maps of the western side of England, he published from his own surveys many large-scale county maps, including those of Herefordshire, Hampshire, Dorset, Worcester and Gloucester. This was a very different operation from the few estate maps by Isaac Taylor of Brentwood, who carefully put his place of residence on his maps.

The name of CHARLES BAYNE of Thorndon is on a 1768 map[188] of two small farms in Baddow belonging to a Mr Shuttleworth of London. The survey by Bayne is dated June 28th. It is a well made map with a good script, beautifully decorated for some words. The unusual feature is the use of two arrows, one pointing north, the other east, as a polar indicator. Nothing more is known of Bayne but his residence in Thorndon immediately suggests some connection with the estates of Lord Petre of Thorndon Hall. There is nothing to turn the suggestion into fact. Petre did have a chief gardener called James Baines in 1742 but that hardly counts.

RICHARD HAWKINS is another name known only from one map;[189] it is assumed that he lived near Brentwood as the survey is of the Weald Hall estate at South Weald, dated 7 May 1743. The map is very crude in execution and its title starts "An ac'urat survey . . ." It shows the lands around Weald Hall's park which was so beautifully mapped in 1738, probably by Bourginion.

Brentwood Schoolmasters

JOHN FITCHATT owned his own school in Brentwood.[190] It is likely that land surveying would have been part of its curriculum. Born in 1729, he may well have been the son or nephew of a Brentwood farmer, Henry Fitchatt. His first map,[191] dated 1750, was of the glebe land of Great Warley, a survey that may have been the fruit of friendship between schoolmaster and parish rector, as the next map does not appear until 1768. This map[192] shows four little areas in Romford and Noak Hill (a total of 58 acres) with a blacksmith's shop clearly drawn in elevation. In 1772 he produced two maps,[193] one with good drawings of the Lion and Lamb and the Robin Hood inns in Brentwood (only 31 acres in all) and the other[194] of a 137 acre farm in Horndon. The maps are devoid of decoration but the good italic script, sometimes embellished with decorative serifs, is pleasing. Obviously land measurement took a back seat to teaching.

Teaching enabled Fitchatt, not himself a university man, to send his son Francis to St John's College, Cambridge,[195] and to buy land in Brentwood and Horndon. In his will, proved in 1776, he left the school to Francis, who had been ordained on graduating from Cambridge. It is most likely that he never succeeded his father as headmaster because there is a titillating note of his leaving for Barbados in 1774 as "he had to go abroad".

JOSIAH TAYLOR styled himself "Philomath" on two of his maps. He was not related to Isaac Taylor of Brentwood. After this Josiah had started surveying Isaac did have a son

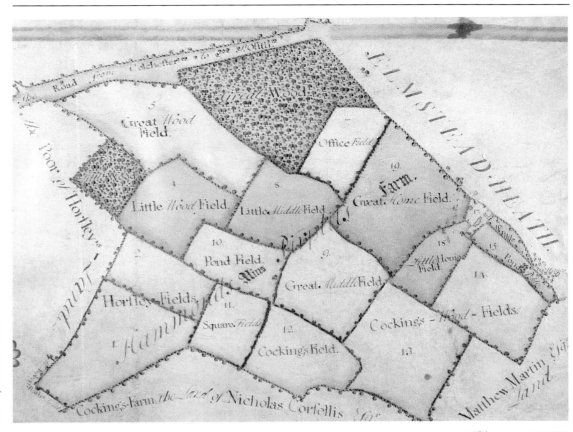

Map of fields in Elmstead by William Brasier (see p. 40), 1730. Note Brasier's subtle use of shading on two sides of the field to give an impression of "depth" (see also illus. p. 38)

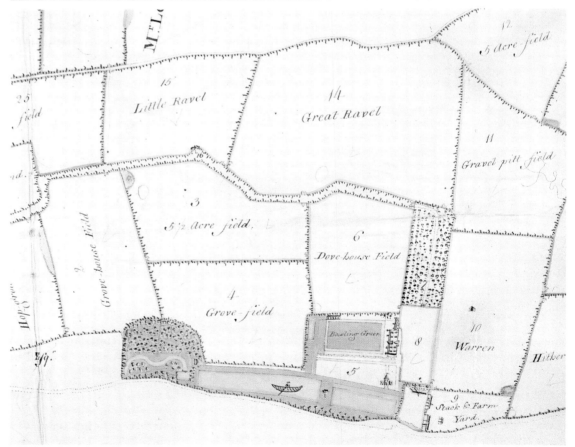

Detail from a map of farms in Great Braxted by Matthew Hall Jnr. (see p. 120), 1777. With its buildings in "collapsed elevation" and crude decorative boat on the lake, the map has an archaic feel. Note the pavilion in the pleasure ground south of the house (See also illus. p. 116).

named Josiah who became a successful London publisher. The areas surveyed by Josiah suggest that he resided either in Brentwood or, equally, in Romford.

The characteristic of his maps was the display of the title on a square flag or mantle, held at the top corners by flying angels. These are not like the more usual static cherub often portrayed but are sufficiently individual to allow a confident attribution of a 1760 map of a 25 acre farm in Stock to Josiah Taylor despite its anonymity.

Taylor's first map, dated 1746, showed a farm in Lambourne (215 a.) and some fields (38 a.) in Chigwell belonging to George Scott, whose father employed Taylor to survey a small Lambourne farm of his in 1752. An unusual spin-off from the 1746 map is a beautifully worked sampler that faithfully copies Taylor's drawing of the fields of the Lambourne farm. The field names are stitched on the fields, unlike the lettered fields of the map. The sampler is lavishly decorated with tendrils, birds and animals. Presumably it was the work of a gifted young daughter of the Scott family. This is the only sampler known in the Victoria and Albert Museum to be a copy of an estate map.

The 1752 map of the oyster grounds at Southchurch was made for Lord Archer of Pyrgo Park, Havering. This map was exactly copied by James Taylor in 1791. James was a London surveyor but the name hints at a possible family link with Josiah Taylor.

Josiah Taylor's maps are all workmanlike in the clear outline of fields and of trees together with an indication of land use. As well as the characteristic cartouche, the scale bar in all the maps is framed by decoration.

TABLE TEN

THE MAPS OF JOSIAH TAYLOR

Date	Parish	Comment	Reference
1746	Lambourne	Farm 216 a. Chigwell 38 a. owned by George Scott	D/DU 666
1749	Fyfield	Farm 172 a.	D/DC 27/1110
1751	Romford	Mill Field 9 a. & Mill	D/DU 461
1752	Southchurch	Oyster grounds, Lord Archer	D/DS 53/1
"	Lambourne	Farm 38 a. for Thomas Scott	D/DLo P1
"	Upminster	"Manor of Gains", 103 a.	D/DZb 5
1760	Stock	Farm 25 a. (Anon. map)	D/DGe P12

Along the Thames

Two names are associated with Dagenham maps. A draft map[196] of 1747 has a remarkable title that suggests a recitation of a written manorial survey. "A survey of the messuages, lands and tenements of Daniel Pilon, Gent. Called the Whale-bone-house held by Copy of Court Roll of the Mannor of Barking; abutting South on Rumford Road near the Whale-bone, East and North on the Blind Lane and West on the lane leading to Marks. Per Thos. Arther, Surveyor." The Whalebone house is drawn in elevation as a three story building. THOMAS ARTHER appears nowhere else. Although the "t" in the name is clearly written there is a lingering suspicion that it might have been a mis-spelling by Thomas Archer, who styled himself in the same way and whose work close to Dagenham has already been described.

NICHOLAS HOWARD surveyed and made a plain map[197] of 40 acres in Dagenham in 1764.

An unusual map,[198] made in 1740, of the "Mannors of Wanstead and Aldersbrook where they are contiguous on each other" was "survey'd and drawn" by RICHARD ARNOLD. The whole "working surface" of the map, normally with untouched blank spaces, is drawn and coloured to give a "natural" look to the land. Wanstead Flats are covered with grass, hummocks and shrubs. The map also shows "Mr Lethieullier's land, late a warren". As John Noble surveyed the whole of the manor of Aldersbrook for Lethieullier in 1740, it is difficult to understand what Arnold was doing there at the same time. A Richard Arnold surveyed a Suffolk estate in 1702 but there is nothing to connect him with the Arnold of Aldersbrook.

"A plan" of John Moseley's 162 a. Dagenham farm was "taken" in 1758 by I. CLEVELEY, otherwise unknown. The map[199] has a rococo cartouche, an achievement of arms and, for no particular reason, a cherub waving a flag.

The surviving work of JOHN WOOD was mostly done between 1746 and 1753. This is after a gap of 17 years from his first two maps. The consistency of his work argues for one man and lost maps rather than a father and son succession. Wood lived in Romford, noted on his 1727 and 1746 maps. On the latter he styled himself surveyor and in 1752 he was "Officer of Excise". This appointment cannot be dated, but it suggests his later career, as only one map follows. He did not work for any owner of large estates. All his surveys are of small farms, around 80 acres, mainly in the neighbourhood of Romford. His first survey was for Mrs Browse who was the daughter of Andrew Branfill of Upminster Hall, and the last was for the ancient Roger Reed charity that supported alms houses in Romford.

Wood was interested in timber, enumerating trees by species on what he called a "pocket map" of a little estate in Hornchurch, and using symbols to show trees by species on his Stisted map. But he disregarded distinction of arable from pasture land. His cartography was crude and his plain maps very plain. When he did use decoration his imagination outran his dexterity. His cartouches look a little oldfashioned with baroque scroll-work. He also used floral motifs in some profusion. Both the 1750 and 1753 maps have the unusual addition of a large hand with a flowing lace cuff that holds the divider above the scale bar.

TABLE ELEVEN

THE MAPS OF JOHN WOOD

Date	Parish	Comment	Reference
1727	Upminster	Two small farms for Mrs Browse	In private hands
1729	Hornchurch	Farm, 24 a. for Prujean	D/DQs 32
1746	" "	Farm 24 a.	D/DU 721/11
c. 1750	Stisted	Farm 81 a.	D/DHt P49
1750	Braintree	Farm 81 a. for J. Brock	T/M 435
1752	White Notley	Farm 69 a. for J. Brock	T/M 202
1753	Romford	Lands of 132 a. for Roger Reed Charity	T/M 302

JOHN CADMAN may have been a cartographer rather than a land measurer. His one Essex map[199] is titled "A plan of the estate called Fanns or Fenns belonging to Capt. John Pelley" and below this is just "J. Cadman, 1755". There is nothing about it being surveyed or drawn by Cadman. This property in Aveley was owned by the Pelley family of West Ham. The map, showing 198 acres of farm land, is quite remarkable for its lavish decoration. The whole is bordered by a good impression of the modern "Hogarth" picture frame. The title and the reference table are enclosed by an intricate framework topped by a pagoda-like structure with a spire and weathervane, with little bells hanging from the roof. This is the only example of the fashionable chinoiserie decoration to adorn an Essex estate map. If that was not enough there is a realistic picture of a house and gardens enclosed by a frame, surmounted by a crest and flanked by drawings of nautical instruments on one side and a sailing ship on the other. Presumably these were a delicate compliment to Capt. Pelley's seafaring. The scripts used on the map are good and very decorative.

Cadman's other surviving maps show a similar love of extreme decoration. They comprise a series of 13 maps[201] depicting the Hertfordshire and Huntingdon estates of the Earl of

Sandwich. The important point is that the survey was undertaken by Warburton and the maps delineated by Cadman. Warburton was a well known surveyor, cartographer and entrepreneur. There is no evidence to show that he ever used Cadman's services again. Cadman's maps for the Earl of Sandwich are dated 1757 and explore all the decorative devices used by him on his 1755 Aveley map. The picture frame borders are even more extensive, the pagoda erection is there as are the vignettes of houses and the collections of instruments (this time they are instruments for survey and not nautical).

Cadman's association with Aveley is difficult to work out. The name Cadman was not uncommon in the families of that part of Essex. One more definite clue is a signed receipt[202] for a manorial fine in the manor of Tilbury. The signature is of J. Cadman, written in a bold artistic hand decorated with serifs. The receipt is signed on behalf of Earl Tylney, the lord of the manor. Tylney's manorial steward was William Carter, so Cadman was filling in for him as some sort of agent for the estate, which suggests that he might also be able to survey. It must not be forgotten that this Cadman may have had nothing to do with the Cadman who made maps, but the associations of name, place and even date (receipt is of August, 1740) do suggest that it is one and the same man at different stages of his life.

References and Notes (Part II Second Period)

1 Documents (C12/363/25) in Public Record Office.
2 D/DNe P3.
3 D/DNe E9.
4 D/DNe E10.
5 From the Catalogues of maps in the Kent and in the Hertfordshire Record Offices.
6 D/DBc P13.
7 D/DL P4.
8 T/M 60/1–6 and D/DEl P86 and D/DH P2.
9 D/DBz P1.
10 D/DU P7.
11 D/DCx P1.
12 D/DQ 43/2.
13 The map is at Audley End.
14 The original map is in the Town Hall, Saffron Walden (also ERO T/M 90).
15 D/DQ 11–14; D/DU 120; T/M 123 & 124.
16 D/DQ 74. This map is huge (80″ by 112″).
17 D/DBy E20.
18 D/DMa P7.
19 The book is in the Guildhall Library.
20 Both maps are in the Guildhall Library.
21 The Minute Book is in the Guildhall Library.
22 D/DU 268/15.
23 D/DBd P1. "Lands belonging to Mowden Hall . . . Survey'd and Drawn by Daniel Halls 1730 and diminished by Edwd Jn° Eyre, Surveyor, 1762."
24 Both original maps in New College, Oxford (ERO T/M 155–156).
25 The original maps are in New College, Oxford; only the Dunmow map has Eyre's name on it, but the other two are identical in style and dated 1768. I am indebted to Miss C. Lane, assistant archivist, New College, for her help with these maps. (Also ERO T/M 508/1–3.)
26 The engraving is in the Guildhall Library.
27 D/DQ 3/1.
28 D/DCm P12. "Jno Woodward Fecit" has an old-fashioned flavour.
29 D/SH 23 & 24.
30 R. Gough; 1780. *British Topography.*
31 D/SH 2.
32 D/SH 18, 19, 21.
33 D/SH 11.
34 D/SH 8.
35 D/DHw P5.
36 Acc. 6319. Bundle 31.
37 D/DSt P4.
38 D/DSa Vol. 1.
39 The map is in the archives of the Marquis of Salisbury.

40 D/DHt P8.
41 Original map in Map Library, British Library (also see ERO T/M 133).
42 T/M 193.
43 T/M 454/1.
44 From the Minute Book of the Governors, in the archives of St Bartholomew's Hospital.
45 Original maps in archives of St Bart's Hospital (ERO T/M 356 & 355).
46 Information kindly supplied by Dr J. Andrews, Trinity College, Dublin.
47 ERO D/DZn 4.
48 P. D. A. Harvey; 1980. *Topographical Maps*. London. Thames & Hudson.
49 The maps by Hawkins are in Hackney Public Library.
50 The traced copies are in Cambridge University Library.
51 D/DQ 14/38.
52 D/DQ 14/192.
53 D/DHt E4.
54 D/DU 737/4.
55 D/DWc P1.
56 D/DL P4.
57 See Dorothy Stroud; 1975. *Capability Brown*. London. Faber & Faber.
58 The history, factual and imagined, is by H. Barty-King; 1975. *Scratch a Surveyor*. London. Heinemann Ltd.
59 Two accounts of Rocque's career are in – a. J. Varley, 1948. *Imago Mundi 5*, 83; b. H. Phillips. *London Topographical Record XX*, 9.
60 The engraved plans are in the Map Library, British Library.
61 J. Andrews; 1978. *Irish Maps*. Dublin. Irish Heritage Series.
62 D/DCw P46.
63 D/P 175/3/1. There was a John Bland (1702–50), a London writing master, but there is no evidence of his being a surveyor. The script of the map is too bad for a writing master.
64 D. Hodson; 1984. *County Atlases of the British Isles*. Tewin Press.
65 D/DC 10/3. The map is accompanied by a written survey.
66 D/SH 16.
67 D/DCw P8.
68 T/M 174.
69 D/DU 557/1.
70 D/DSg T3.
71 F. Hull; 1954. *Geographical Journal*.
72 T/M 436. Original map in Vestry Museum, Walthamstow.
73 T/M 403. Original map in Hertfordshire Record Office.
74 T/M 167. Original in Vestry Museum.
75 For discussion of Hill's Essex maps see K. Neale, *Chingford Notes* Vol. I. no. 8 & 9.
76 The maps are in the Hertfordshire Record Office.
77 D/DJg P1.
78 D/DHe P1.
79 D/DB P37.
80 D/DPo P2.
81 From *Dictionary of Land Surveyors*, Op. cit.
82 D/DR P9.
83 D/DEl P8.
84 D/DOt P5.
85 D/DQy 4.
86 The map is in Audley End.
87 The map is in the Suffolk Record Office.
88 D/DEl P6.
89 Map in Suffolk Record Office.
90 Map in Suffolk Record Office.
91 D/DWV P6.
92 Map in Suffolk Record Office.
93 D/DBr P1.
94 D/DMb P5.
95 D/DCd P1.
96 From *Dictionary of Land Surveyors*. Op. cit.

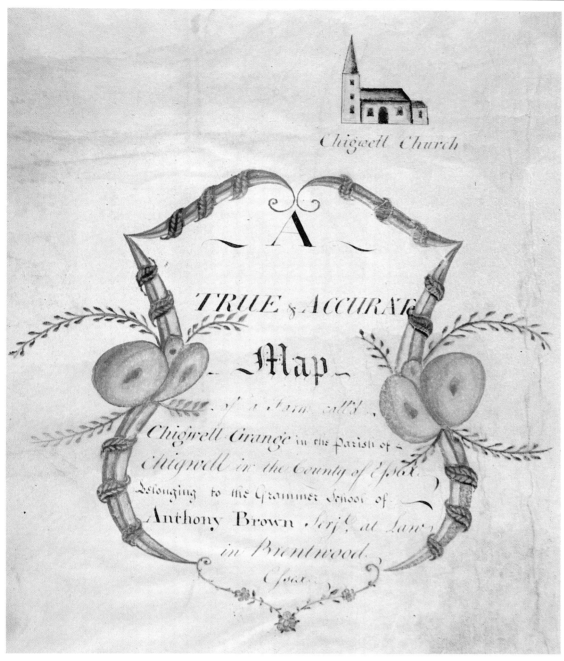

Chigwell Church

A TRUE & ACCURATE Map ... of a farm call'd Chigwell Grange in the parish of Chigwell in the County of Essex belonging to the Grammer School of Anthony Brown Serj.t at Law in Brentwood, Essex.

Simple but elegant cartouche with peaches and leaves by George Sangster, (see p. 86), 1769. (See also illus. p. 54).

97 Morant states that Sir William Wake died in 1765. So the surveys, noting him as the land owner, must have been done for his heir.

98 D/DHt P12.

99 D/DHt P13.

100 See D/DL P7.

101 D/DGo P1.

102 I am grateful to Mr D. M. M. Shorrocks, Somerset County Archivist, for his expert comparison of the Shalford map with the Fairchild maps in the Somerset Record Office.

103 Map in Kent Record Office.

104 Map in Suffolk Record Office.

105 D/DQy 3 (unfortunately this map is now missing).

106 D/DRb P2.

107 D/DOt P1, 2, 3.

108 D/DEl P16.

109 Information kindly supplied by Mr J. Bensusan-Butt.

110 T/M 317.

111 T/M 250.

112 Advertisement in the *Ipswich Journal*.

113 The Suffolk Record Office kindly searched but could not find any relevant reference.

114 D/DR P11.

115 D/DEl P13.

116 D/DEl P14.

117 D/DR P12.

118 D/DEl P8.

119 D/DTu 201.

120 D/DK P10.

121 In 1767 "An estimate of Colne Engayne" was recorded in a written survey by Owen Swan (ERO D/P 193/3/1).

122 The map is in the Guildhall Library together with a pair of maps of the Dean and Chapter's farms in Belchamp St Pauls. The two maps are in the same hand but anonymous and undated, probably circa 1780. It is possible that they were made from surveys by Storer.

123 D/DHt P14.

124 D/DHt P17.

125 D/DCm E2.

126 D/DHt P29.

127 D/DHt P28.

128 D/DHt P18.

129 T/M 297. The original map is at Gosfield Hall.

130 In a letter of 1783 to Sir T. Spencer-Wilson Storer wrote "I have for nine years past made the agreements for Lord Nugent's farms belonging to his Gosfield Hall estates."

131 Microfilm T/M 293.

132 This field book is now unknown but is referred to in the notes added to the 1772 map.

133 D/DDc A22 fol. 60.

134 D/DU 19/11.

135 D/DDc P9/1–5.

136 D/DFr P1–5.

137 D/DFr A3/5–8.

138 D/DBm P9.

139 T/M 485/3. The original map was made for Thomas Sewell and is still in the possession of the Sewell family.

140 The map is in the Guildhall Library.

141 D/DCm P25.

142 D/DOp P3 & 4.

143 D/DSm P14.

144 The map is in the Suffolk Record Office.

145 All advertisements of his activities were in the *Chelmsford Chronicle*.

146 His will is in the ERO.

147 Facts taken from the relevant Land Tax Returns.

148 From the Excise archives, Public Record Office.

149 The will is in the ERO.

150 D/DP P105.

151 D/DOp P2.

152 D/DMa P4.

153 D/DGe P9/1.

154 D/DEs P1.

155 D/DPo P1.

156 Data from Land Tax Returns.

157 T/M 459.

158 The map is in the Suffolk Record Office.

159 D/DB P43.

160 The will is in the ERO.

161 ERO T/M 438.

162 See D/DU 649/7.

163 "Copy of the Plan and Contents of Little Baddow Common . . . taken from the Old Map." The copy

was made for an agreement between the Lords of the manors and their tenants respecting enclosure of the Common (see D/DRa 771).

164 Advertisement quoted in a letter (1947) to Dr Emmison from Mr F. Richwood. Subsequent search has failed to identify the advertisement.

165 D/DDc E15/1–3. Written timber survey etc. for Du Cane.

166 I am grateful to Miss G. L. Beech, assistant keeper of maps, Public Record Office, for discovering these facts.

167 There is a copy of this engraving in the Bodleian Library, Oxford.

168 D/P 363/3.

169 Details taken from the minute book of the Commissioners in the GLC Record Office.

170 Raymond purchased these lands in 1755, the year of Skynner's survey. On the map is written "This map was corrected and added to in 1770." That year was too late for Skynner to have altered the map.

171 D/DMy 15M50/90.

172 D/DMa 15M50/104.

173 D/DMa 15M50/267/2.

174 A copy is in the ERO.

175 Skynner's letters to Ray are in the Bedfordshire Record Office.

176 The will is in the ERO.

177 Advertisement in *Chelmsford Chronicle*.

178 D/DLa M60.

179 Brown founded Brentwood Grammar School in 1558 and his founding gift was the Chigwell Grange estate.

180 D/DHt P50.

181 C/TS 62.

182 D/DK P8.

183 D/DGe P11.

184 The map is in the Hertfordshire Record Office.

185 See D. M. Armitage; 1939. *The Taylors of Ongar*, also *The Family Pen* ed. Isaac Taylor 1867 and the *Autobiography and other memorials of Mrs Gilbert*, 1878 (all are in the ERO).

186 The map is in the Hertfordshire Record Office.

187 The map is in the Map Library, British Library.

188 D/DU 77/10.

189 D/DTw P2.

190 The details are in his will (in the ERO).

191 The map is listed in the Guide to Parish Records in the ERO. Recent search for the map, said to be in the hands of the parish, proved unsuccessful.

192 D/DHe P2.

193 D/DBe P1.

194 D/DS 127/2.

195 Noted in Venn's *Alumni Cantab*.

196 D/DSa P153.

197 T/M 91/1.

198 D/DSa P152.

199 The map is in Valence House Museum, Dagenham.

200 T/M 28. The original map is in Aveley Hall.

201 Copies of these maps are in the Map Library, British Library.

202 D/DCm E14.

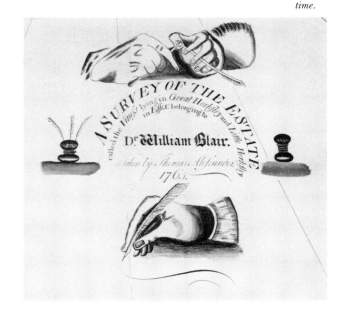

An unusual cartouche by Thomas Alefounder (see p. 76), 1765, breaking away from more common themes to use a hand and pen motif beloved of the writing masters of the time.

THIRD PERIOD (1770–99)
Surveyors From outside Essex

LONDON BASED

LONDON SURVEYORS PROBABLY provide the key to the anonymity of two major series of Essex estate maps, distinguished by the large areas surveyed and the similarity of their elegant cartography. One series was made in 1783 for Christ's Hospital. Four maps show the Hospital's lands in the parishes of a) Berden, b) Langley, c) Ugley and Rickling, and d) Clavering. Each map outlines the parish boundaries and shows the Hospital's lands in great detail. The other series of anonymous maps were made for Lord Petre and show his lands as follows –

1777	Stock; whole of parish	(D/DP P29)
1779	Stock; 400 a. of Petre land	(D/DP P34)
"	Stock; 865 a. " " "	(D/DP P33)
"	Ingatestone; whole parish	(D/DP P31)
"	Margaretting; Sth of parish	(D/DP P32)
Undated	Mountnessing; whole of parish	(D/DP P27)
"	Writtle & Roxwell; about 3000 a.	(D/DP P35)

A simple polar indicator and a decorative flower from a map of Crickits Farm, Witham by Benjamin Fallowes (see p. 48), 1716. The use of simple decorative devices, unrelated to the map and "floating" in the margin died out as the century progressed.

These maps are referred to in the valuation book of Lord Petre's Essex estates that was written in 1781. So the undated maps must have been made before this year.

On comparison of style Dr Emmison[1] considered that both series were by the same hand. Again on grounds of style, Dr Hyde[2] of the Guildhall Library attributed the Christ's Hospital maps to THOMAS BAINBRIDGE. The opinions of both experts would appear to be correct if judged solely by one decorative theme. Very fine pen and ink drawings of a man holding an axe and resting amongst trees is on the Langley map for Christ's Hospital and varied slightly in the Petre map of Writtle, the same style being found on the 1777 Stock map depicting a couple resting by a stream and looking at a house and park across the water. These pictures are exactly reproduced in the maps[3] made for the Earl of Shrewsbury in 1789–9 by Thomas Bainbridge. The two series of maps are linked by the similarity in layout and the naturalistic display of arable and pasture land, in the sparse use of colour and the excellent scripts, particularly in the roman capitals. The cartouches are mainly Adamesque just as used by Bainbridge and JOHN FOAKES, who were the named surveyors for Christ's Hospital in their maps[4] of 1789–90. When these land surveyors worked together it was always as Foakes and Bainbridge.

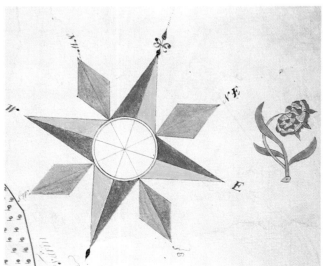

An unusually decorative polar indicator by John Lee (see p. 50), from a map of lands in Birdbrook, 1726. The miniature globe in the centre substitutes for the more common floral motif and contrasts strongly with Fallowes' extreme simplicity (p. 98)

A further link between the two series of maps is provided by JOSEPH BUTLER, who started his career in the City of York. He must have had an early interest in London because in 1771–2 advertisements in the *Chelmsford Chronicle* of land for sale directed enquirers to Mr Lloyd of Gray's Inn, London, or to Mr Butler, surveyor at York. Around 1775 Butler moved to London. By 1785, in advertisements of land for sale, he gave his address as Gray's Inn, the same address as given by Foakes and Bainbridge a little later.

Butler's association with the Christ's Hospital survey is quite clear.[5] In 1783 the Hospital's recurring tithe disputes reached a peak and counsel's opinion was sought on whether grass and clover seeds were part of the great tithe. On this arcane point counsel pronounced that "everything that is either mowed or reaped or otherwise severed from the ground and gathered together in a stack or into a barn as a crop is deemed a great tithe." The Essex tenants, with the persistence of barrack-room lawyers, wanted to know the legal position if they left the seeds to fall from the plants. "Standing to seed" said counsel "came under the small tithe." To quell further argument the Hospital, on 14 May 1783, decided to "appoint a skillfull person to examine" the lands and tithes of the Essex estates. Joseph Butler was chosen as such a man, and he completed his work by the end of that year.

On 7 April 1784 the hospital governors and the tenants were reconciled thanks to "the valuation made on an accurate survey by Mr Joseph Butler". In December of that year Butler was paid the princely sum of £650 for his work. Butler, who styled himself "surveyor", not "land surveyor", appears never to have made a map. He could never have completed his work for Christ's Hospital in such a short time unless he employed assistants. What he paid them was presumably reflected in his large bill. It is reasonable to suppose that he used Bainbridge, and perhaps Foakes, for the land measurement and the maps.

Butler's association with Lord Petre was earlier and different, but no less direct. Petre wished to enclose some land in West Horndon and obtained the necessary Act of Parliament to do so.[6] The Commissioners appointed for this enclosure first met in March 1776. Joseph Butler was the only surveyor of the three Commissioners and must have chosen the surveyor, as Smithson Dawson "of the City of York, land surveyor" was appointed. It is most unlikely that a man from York would have undertaken the prolonged work involved and so would have relied on assistants. The final award, together with a good but undecorated map, was dated 3 August 1778 but it was not enrolled until the next year. Each statement by the Commissioners and the whole bundle of documents were signed by two witnesses, one of whom was John Foakes. It is of note that the years covering the whole process of enclosure fit exactly with the years in which the series of anonymous maps were made for Lord Petre. Foakes certainly was on site, and possibly Bainbridge as his close associate. It is reasonable to surmise that these two were responsible for the maps, made from surveys when they were not immediately concerned with the slow legal process of enclosure. If so, they would have been in the early years of their careers, which later developed at the same address as given by Butler. Maybe they provided the expertise in land management and cartography that Butler needed in his assistants. Bainbridge's later career was often concerned with enclosure, usually as the surveyor, occasionally as a Commissioner.

SAMUEL and RICHARD WILLIAMS, presumably brothers, worked from Holborn mainly for church authorities. For the Dean and Chapter of St Paul's Samuel surveyed the manor of Barling in 1766 (and also in Barnes, Surrey, 1769) and Richard surveyed in Laindon[7] in 1776. In those years St Paul's employed London surveyors for lands near London but used local surveyors for the more distant estates; thus Storer of Halstead surveyed in Wickham St Paul's, not far from his home. Samuel also worked for the Dean and Chapter of St George's Chapel, Windsor, surveying[8] their three manors in Dagenham in 1772, the year in which Richard surveyed[9] 1130 acres of Sir Anthony Abdy's land in White Roding and Stapleford.

Richard and Samuel Williams used the same style of cartography, with beautiful if slightly old fashioned cartouches. Their excellent flower and frond paintings are on a par with Woodward's 1769 cartouche. Samuel's Barling map is intriguing in that the polar indicator, a star within a circle, looks as if it had been drawn by a schoolboy with ruler and compass, but the gilded and highly coloured floral cartouche is exquisitely painted.

DANIEL MUMFORD and JOHN DOYLEY are linked as master and pupil. Mumford worked up to 1799 and Doyley's career flourished well in to the 19th century. Both surveyed widely in southern England.

Mumford's first known survey, dated 1778, was so large a commission and so mature in its execution that his career is likely to have started some time before that date. The survey was of James Blackmore's Essex estate in Nettleswell (1520 a.). The survey was presented in two forms.[10] The whole estate was depicted on one large map mounted on a roller. Below the title is written "D. Mumford, survey'd & delint." This map is a recent accession to the Essex Record Office and gives an identity to a book of 44 maps of the same date showing the estate piece by piece. The book is anonymous and has been in the Record Office for many years. Content and style indicate that it is the other presentation by Mumford.

Two years later he was back in Essex with a survey of the hamlet of Thundersley, Wimbish, "Purchased in 1779 by Thos. Wolfe Esq; made in 1780 by D. Mumford, land surveyor".[11] He was not in Essex again until 1794, when with Doyley he surveyed[12] three farms in Helion Bumpstead, the land extending into Cambridgeshire. A year later Mumford alone surveyed the whole parish of Widdington, his map now known from the revised copy used as the 1839 tithe map. In 1796 and 1798 he and Doyley worked for Tylney-Long of Wanstead. They surveyed his estates in Felsted when William Cole of Colchester was surveying his estate in Rochford. The Felsted survey was shown on three large decorated maps[13] and a fourth map[14] that is a plain draft. The decorated maps have "Surveyed by Danl. Mumford". The same legend is on the draft but a pencilled insert has "by Jno. Doyley Assistant to" before Mumford. The map is endorsed "Rec^d from Mr William Doyley 4th October 1862", a descendant who wanted John Doyley's role made clear. He need not have worried as there is a book of 18 maps[15] entitled "Plans of several farms and lands situate in the parishes of Felsted and Great Waltham . . . surveyed by John Doyley, 1796". These maps show many of the properties shown on the four Felsted maps and some extra lands. The title page has a fine rococo "mirror-frame" decoration surmounted by a human face surrounded by rays, a style used by Mumford.

Illustration, page 102

Illustration, page 73

The year 1798 was a busy one in Essex for Mumford. With Doyley he surveyed Fyfield Hall for Tylney-Long, the map[16] having "J. Doyley Delin." He also surveyed farms belonging to Nathaniel Hillier in St Osyth and Weeley (408 acres) and Brightlingsea (275 acres). These surveys are known from the copied maps[17] made by one of the Surveyor-General's draftsmen in 1804 when the Crown purchased the properties.

Mumford also surveyed in that year the manor of Rickland, lying in Rickland and Oakley, belonging to James Raymond and Lady Falkland. Lady Falkland was the daughter of Richard Chiswell of Debden, who died in 1787 leaving his holding of the manor to her. The odd part of the story is that the map of this survey is now in the library of the University of British Columbia, Vancouver. It came to the University recently when the Vancouver City Library cleared out unsorted documents from its basement. There is no clue as to how the map got to Canada in the first place. The map is typical of Mumford's pleasing style, in which the use of a green wash along the field boundaries gives an attractive and distinctive appearance to the "working surface", which also has good scripts. Mumford's cartouches are all well drawn with Adamesque decorations of flower chains and ribbon. This style was quite common and used, for instance, by Foakes and Bainbridge. Mumford's style was set by the time he made his 1778 map and did not vary over the years. Doyley kept to the same style for his cartouches.

John Doyley continued to flourish after Mumford gave up work and maintained his contacts with the Tylney-Long family. He made huge maps[18] of extensive surveys of the family's estates in Wanstead, Woodford and Leyton in 1812 and 1815. By that time he gave his address as Gray's Inn. Doyley's son became a surveyor, starting as an assistant to James Asser of Dartford, Kent. There is an 1825 map[19] of Prittlewell that was made by "John Doyley, surveyor, assistant to James Asser".

A group of four successful London surveyors each made one major Essex survey. In 1771 THOMAS PRIDE surveyed and mapped[20] a 1900 acre estate in and around Woodham Ferrers that Charles Raymond was then in the process of buying. The large map, on a roller, shows the whole estate on a scale of 20″ to one mile. The cartography is conventional and of the time. Pride worked from King Street, Bloomsbury, surveying from 1758 in the home counties and also in the west.

ISAAC MESSIDER surveyed[21] in 1774 the manor of Runwell, comprising virtually the whole parish. The state of cultivation is shown on the map, which explains that the manor is "more particularised in the field book of the plan". The book is missing. For the Bishopric of London, in 1775, he surveyed "Curds farm near Billarica" and a farm in Tilbury. Both maps[22] have "Isaac Messider Snr, surveyor and delineator". Working from Hampstead, he used "senior" from 1754 to 1784, but what "junior" did is unknown.

JOHN MIDDLETON of Lambeth surveyed in 1788–9 the manor and whole parish of South Weald. The map,[23] another one on a roller, measures 106 by 80 inches. Much of the mapping is done with a brush, not a pen. The title is enclosed in an ellipse around which is a monochrome sylvan scene with a bridge on one side and a house by a lake on the other. Scattered on the ground are agricultural implements and above the ellipse is a bird with a flower chain in its beak. A complementary map[24] to this shows in detail the houses of Brentwood town which are sketched on the main map. Each house is shown in block plan but the gardens are drawn in detail, even showing each tree as deciduous or coniferous. This map is anonymous, but in style is clearly by Middleton.

The South Weald survey was the only rural land survey made by Middleton. His busy career, from 1782 to 1833, has been researched by Gus Edwards,[25] who showed that Middleton was a surveyor of London parishes and manors in or near Lambeth and that he was primarily concerned with buildings and the legal problems of ownership. So he described

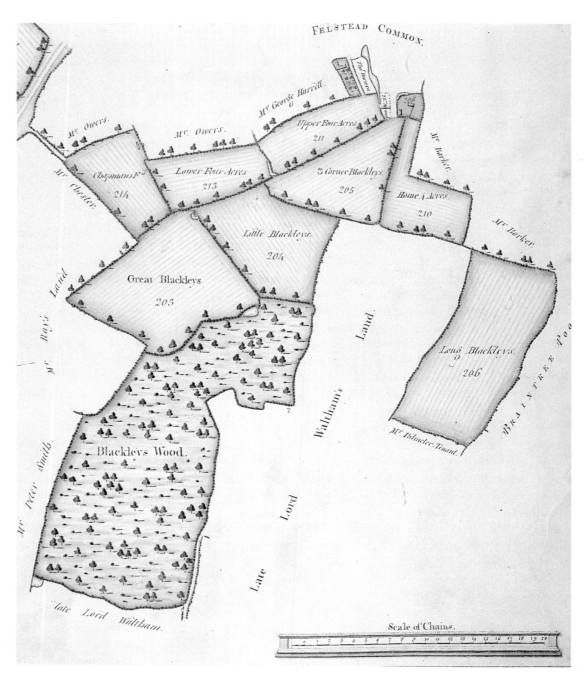

Fields in Felsted from a map by Daniel Mumford (see p. 100), 1796.

himself as a surveyor, but not a land surveyor. Colvin[26] states that Charles Barry, architect of the House of Commons, was indentured to Middleton in 1810.

Middleton also figures in a minor Essex cartographic mystery. When (1792) Harrison wanted to improve the park of his recently acquired estate in Stanway he commissioned the ageing Richard Woods to plan the changes. This was Woods' last work and he had already retired as a landscape gardener to be Lord Petre's surveyor at Thorndon. The land concerned had been surveyed and mapped by George Hutson of Shenfield in 1787. Woods wrote to Harrison to tell him that he had seen Hutson and "he very civilly showed me his survey of the Manor of Stanway but would not by any means part with it out of his own hands but will let me have a copy of that part of the estate that you have purchased in the course of about three weeks". This letter[27] was written by Woods on 20 August 1792. Hutson's original decorated map had been made for Bellamy, from whom Harrison purchased his part. Presumably this could have been available to Harrison. Hutson did not make his promised copy, for Woods' improvements were roughly drawn on an outline map[28] in fine pen. The contents table and the cartouche are in Woods' hand and stuck onto the map. At the bottom, in the fine pen of the map itself, is a scale bar with a divider above which has across it a well drawn pencil on which is written "J. Middleton". This decoration was not used by Middleton on any of the maps of his own surveys and suggests that he drew this map from Hutson's notes and draft. Anyway Woods charged Harrison for a plan, survey and his improvements.

RICHARD HORWOOD of Mare Street, Hackney, is best known for his large scale surveys of London parishes. Sometime in the mid-1790s he surveyed for Lord Waldegrave the manor and whole parish of Navestock. This work is known from a revised copy[29] of his map made in 1835.

SPURRIER and PHIPPS were the surveyors of the whole parish of Beauchamp Roding in 1794, by "order of Robt. Gaussen Esq (Impropriator)", which indicates that the survey was for the purpose of tithing. The map[30] has a pleasant Adamesque cartouche topped with a drape. There is an interesting note to state that "The estate of James Bingham entitles proprietor to liberty of Hawking, Hunting, Shooting, Fishing and Fowling within the limits of the County of Essex."

John Spurrier of Throgmorton Street was much more of an estate agent than a land surveyor. In the decade from the mid-1770s he was in partnership with Sampson selling and auctioning properties. In 1781 they were selling proprietor's shares in the Stour River Navigation Company. But in the 1790s it was the partnership of Spurrier and Phipps that was busy selling property.

A number of London surveyors did only small surveys in Essex. JOHN WILLOCK surveyed[31] just 50 acres in Little Tey (1770) at the start of his career. Like Spurrier, he was primarily an agent for property sales, although he always described himself as a land surveyor. He worked from New Burlington Street up to about 1780 and from then on at Golden Square. He was a constant advertiser of land for sale in the *Chelmsford Chronicle*, and in 1796 was asked to write and place advertisements for the sale of Beeleigh Mill.

JAMES WYBURD surveyed[32] 370 acres in Epping in 1794. The map is neat but with minimal decoration. Wyburd also surveyed in counties near to London. His name appeared in a 1788 announcement[33] of the partnership formed by Wyburd and Jacques in Hatton Gardens in which Richard Jacques "surveyor, broker, appraiser and auctioneer" with 17 years' experience in the business said that he would combine his skills with Wyburd's knowledge of land surveying. Such a partnership was not confined to London; Storer did the same thing in Halstead. Several Essex land surveyors took up selling and auctioneering themselves. There does not appear to be an example of an auctioneer turning to land surveying.[34]

JAMES TAYLOR of Chancery Lane was another whose one Essex survey came early in his career. His 1776 map[35] of a Dengie farm has an Adam style cartouche and the contents table lists the timber according to species of tree. Much later, in 1791, he copied[36] Josiah Taylor's

1752 map of the oyster grounds at Southchurch. The map has a nice Adam medallion above the scale bar but is notable for the water-colour picture of men and boats on the foreshore that was pasted on to a blank space of the map. This makes it unlikely that Taylor painted the picture, which is a composition on its own. The association of James and Josiah Taylor may be a coincidence of names but prompts the thought of a family link.

LEONARD SEARLES, a carpenter from Greenwich, founded a family of surveyors. His map[37] of Wanstead Park (1779) follows the Adam style with its cartouche. The Tylneys seemed to have had all sorts of surveyors at Wanstead during the century. Why another map of the Park was made is a mystery.

JOSEPH SPARROW surveyed[38] a small farm in Kelvedon Hatch in 1776. Later he surveyed in Kent. His inclusion as a Londoner is based on a guess that he was related to Thomas and John Sparrow, both land surveyors of Hammersmith. Thomas Sparrow published his town plan of Colchester in 1767 and proposed to survey the whole county of Essex, a plan that came to nothing.

JOHN PRICKETT of Highgate is probably under-represented by his surviving Essex work. One field of two acres in Barling (1775) and 32 acres of farm in Bulphan (1796) are such tiny portions as to suggest that these maps[39] survive from more extensive surveys. He did better in 1797–8 surveying the more extensive estate of Frances Cotton in Horndon and Laindon. The three maps[40] covering the survey are neat, well scripted and plain. The land owner's name is omitted from the titles, although a space was left for its inclusion.

Prickett was an important copier of Essex estate maps. In 1790 he copied the 1690 map by Daynes of Little Hallsbury, in 1792 Cleer's map of Kelvedon (1701) and in 1797 Browne's 1751 map of Wrabness. The first two copies were made for London institutions, the last for a private land owner. The copies show Prickett's considerable skill as a cartographer, with fine austere classical lines.

Prickett's property in Highgate was leased from Christ's Hospital (he put a guinea in the Hospital's poor box to seal the bargain) but he was never employed as surveyor to the Hospital.[41] Like many other surveyors, Prickett bought and sold property. In 1799 he was selling property in Rochford and Brentwood, adding that plans of the estates were available in his office.[42]

As a connection between carpenters and surveyors was quite common in the 18th century it is of interest to find that Holden's Directory of 1799 lists John Prickett as auctioneer and land surveyor of Highgate and, also of Highgate, Charles Prickett, carpenter and A. Prickett, carpenter, and joiner.

WILLIAM JUPP was a London carpenter turned architect and surveyor.[43] The Ironmongers' Company commissioned him and JOHN DUGLEBY, a surveyor from Deptford, to survey its properties in East Ham (1769) and West Ham (1778). The land was mainly agricultural and the resulting two maps[44] are delightful, though very different. The East Ham map was decorated in grey wash. The cartouche is unduly large, depicting a river bank with trees and three men waving at the Company's ceremonial barge being rowed past with a huge flag bearing the Company's arms. The title is written on a stone tablet that dwarfs the men waving. The contents table, which lists each parcel of land under "computed" (total 284 a.) and "measurement" (total 344 a.) acreage, is inscribed on a hanging drape suspended from a pole held in the beak of an eagle. The "working surface", scripts and other details of the map are undistinguished.

All the scripts used in the West Ham map reach the highest standards of late 18th century calligraphy. The cartouche is a grey frame of flowers and foliage, topped by a young man's face surrounded by rays (a design used by John Doyley). The map is dominated by a gilded and brightly coloured achievement of the Company's arms. The table of contents is framed by a painted chain appearing to be held by large nails driven into the paper. The "working surface", showing only 67 acres, is equally fine in its execution, particularly of the boundaries and trees. Under the cartouche is written "Tomkins scripsit". Although "Delint." would be the usual word for someone who drew the map, comparison of the East and West Ham maps strongly suggests that Tomkins was responsible for the whole of the West Ham map, not just for the calligraphy. The name Tomkins covers two artists of the time, both known for their topographical views of London.[45] William Tomkins of Cavendish Square died in 1790 and his son Charles, born around 1750, died in 1810. The map's date of 1778 favours William as the artist who made it. It is a rare example of an artist expressing the findings of a land survey, and the excellent result is oddly unlike the contemporary cartography of land surveyors.

William Jupp was far more an architect (he designed The London Tavern) than a land surveyor. He was the sole surveyor of the Ironmongers' houses in Stepney, whereas Dugleby was employed by the Haberdashers' Company to survey their farms in Staffordshire. However Dugleby was the surveyor to St Thomas' Hospital, although not employed to survey their country estates. Jupp's son followed in father's footsteps and was the architect-surveyor for several City companies, including the Ironmongers. A small-time country carpenter who surveyed was Daniel Warner of Bishop's Stortford. But of the many land surveys done by Londoners Jupp appears to be the only architect involved, and he worked only on the fringe of the City and with a colleague.

At the end of the century JONATHAN GRIST of Old Cavendish Street surveyed in Essex, mainly for official bodies. In 1799, for the Dean and Chapter of St Paul's, he surveyed[45] Tillingham Hall and the marshes with the duck "decoy with ye saltings lately inclosed and embanked from the sea". His long title recites how these lands were vested under the will of William Clarke (1679) and uses the same wording found in the title of two anonymous maps[47] (by the same hand) of the same lands made in 1739. Grist's map is huge and mounted on a roller. The big lettering of the title is a fine example of calligraphy at the turn of the century. The main decorative feature is the duck decoy pictured in the centre of the map. The opening of three netted tunnels is shown across the water with ducks flying above. A man with a duck in his hand is walking away with his dog. A more realistic picture of the decoy is on the 1739 map, which shows the seven tunnels (as on the Ordnance Survey map of 1879) and ducks swimming. A man with his dog watches the scene. This decoy was one of the three Essex decoys (of about 40) still used at the end of the 19th century.

In 1800 Grist surveyed the parishes[48] of Willingale Doe and Beauchamp Roding and also a 152 acre farm[49] that crossed the borders of these parishes. The farm was the only small survey that he made in Essex. For the Commissioners of Sewers, Grist surveyed Foulness Island[50] in 1801 to show newly reclaimed land. This very large map has the outdated device of a divider set over the scale bar. An undated map[51] by Grist illustrates a Tudor survey of Great Tey. This was prepared for Thomas Astle, the lord of the manor, who was delving into the history of his land.

Grist's trade card[52] set out his expertise, particularly "Fens and marshy lands drained. Coal and other mines estimated. Common fields divided. Tithes adjusted between clergymen and their parishioners." Apart from

Illustration page 134

Elaborate rococo cartouche by Edward John Eyre (see p. 65), 1762. Note how the garden theme is carried through from the map to the cartouche, a frequent characteristic of maps of the period (see also illus. p. 42).

measuring timber, he would buy or sell it on commission. The breadth of his activities indicates how far land surveyors were moving away from land measurement alone. Grist's card is undated and gives his address as 121 Oxford Street. Around 1808 he left London and settled in Canterbury and there took his son in to the business.

THE SURVEYOR-GENERAL

Crown land surveyed in Essex during this time was under the direction of the Surveyor-General[53] who employed free-lance surveyors paid at the good daily rate of two pounds. The post of Surveyor-General dates back to 1554 when the Court of Augmentation was abolished. Then two Surveyors-General were appointed to administer Crown woods, one for woods north of the River Trent and the other for woods south of the river. The post of Surveyor-General of Crown lands was revived in 1625; he was responsible for survey and valuation. For example there is Davies' 1745 survey of "His Majesty's lands . . . in Harwich. Surveyed by virtue of a Warrant from the Hon'ble Thomas Walker, Surveyor General of His Majesty's Lands". In 1715 all Crown woods came under the control of one Surveyor-General of Woods who, unlike the Crown land surveyor, was responsible for collecting revenue derived from the woodlands. A common administration appears to have served the surveyors of land and wood. Eventually, in 1810, the Surveyors-General were superseded by a Board of Commissioners of Woods, Forests and Land Revenue.

Polar indicator with border of cherubs by Edward John Eyre (see p. 65) from his map of the Earl of Rochford's parks and gardens in St Osyth's 1762 (see illus. pp. 42 and 105).

THOMAS RICHARDSON of Cavendish Square surveyed[54] Crown land in Leyton (1777; 159 a. farm) and Barking (1781 and 1784; two small farms). Richardson flourished from 1771 to the late 1780s. A notable work of his for the Crown was the survey of the New Forest in 1789 conducted with Abraham and William Driver.

ABRAHAM and WILLIAM DRIVER were the sons of Samuel Driver and greatly extended the family's surveying business while maintaining their nursery garden in the Old Kent Road. In 18th century Essex Abraham surveyed a parcel of Crown land in Havering (1797) and they both surveyed a Crown farm in East Ham[55] (1799). In all the Drivers made 48 Crown surveys, most of them between 1800 and 1835. One of these needs a mention. Their 1814 map[56] (it is more of a chart) of "The Leigh Swatch as staked out with its beacons" was made from a plan of 1762. The Swatch is a channel running between Canvey Island and the mainland. The 1762 plan was made by J. Barrow, who was probably a draftsman for the Crown; there is no evidence that he was an 18th century surveyor.

JOSEPH PENNINGTON is another surveyor whose work in Essex was solely for the Crown. His survey[57] (1787) of a Crown farm in West Ham is shown on a map that states the plan is drawn from a survey by him. His really major work, from 1791 to 1793, was the survey[58] of Hainault Forest. Again, he did not draw the map. It was done by Samuel Baker who was often employed as a Crown draftsman. Pennington surveyed very widely over southern England and in the 1780s was living in Needham Market, Suffolk, a county in which he made many surveys.

MEN FROM KENT

AFTER A LAPSE of years a handful of Essex farms were surveyed by men from Kent. In 1773 a small farm in Roxwell was "surveyed, delineated and admeasured"[59] by WILLIAM JEMMETT of Ashford, Kent.

The Wardens of Rochester Bridge employed HENRY HOGBEN[60] to survey their lands in Kent, and, in 1796, to survey[61] the manor of South Hall in Tilbury. The only decoration on this map is a basket of flowers over the table of contents. An undated plain version[62] of the map also exists. Henry was one of a family of Kent surveyors, his father, Thomas, being a schoolmaster-surveyor. Working at one time with Henry Hogben was THOMAS BUDGEN who in 1792 surveyed a farm in Kelvedon and made a most pleasing map.[63] His scripts were well decorated, and, like Henry Hogben, he did not have a cartouche for the title but used one decorative feature. Budgen's polar indicator has in its centre a lively cherub blowing a trumpet from which hangs a large trumpet cloth. The year after his trip to Essex he moved down to Lewes in Sussex and surveyed widely in the South of England and down to Warwickshire.[64]

JAMES ASSER made a much larger contribution to Essex surveying. His Kent maps date from 1781 and he was well established when, in 1793, for the Commissioners of Sewers, he surveyed[65] Canvey Island, styling himself as "Land Surveyor and Valuer of Estates at Greenhythe near Dartford, Kent". In the next year he surveyed[66] John Judd's North Benfleet Hall and began to use the *Chelmsford Chronicle* to advertise land for sale, starting with leasehold land in Kent. This included his own leasehold property, a "neat substantial dwelling house with lawn, garden, yard and orchard and stable containing one acre, let to Mr James Asser, land surveyor, yearly rent £20". In subsequent advertisements he offered land for sale in Sussex and Cambridgeshire, so he had wide contacts as an estate agent (in the modern sense).

Asser returned to Thames-side Essex in 1798, surveying in March two farms in West Thurrock[67] and in October a road diversion[68] in West Tilbury. The maps of all these surveys are plain and neat. His major Essex survey was after this artificial time boundary, being made in 1802. Then he went up to Bardfield and Finchingfield to survey[69] the large estate of Sir Charles Burrell. Asser's decorations of this map are an exact copy of Bernard Scalé's style, from the script with serif additions for the title which is framed by a "torn paper" design to the polar indicator set with agricultural instruments. The "working surface" of the map is not so well drawn as it would have been by Scalé, but the whole map gives strong credence to the suggestion that Asser had been Scalé's pupil.

The Burrell estate had been surveyed by Skynner when it was in the possession of Charles Raymond. Sylvia Raymond, poetess, dramatist and Charles' eldest daughter, married Sir William Burrell of Beckenham, Kent, and the son of this marriage was Sir Charles Burrell, the estate passing to the Burrells in 1789.

James Asser surveyed widely in southern England and was active up to 1814 (including further surveys in Essex). John Doyley junior was his assistant at the end of his career.[70]

MEN FROM HERTFORDSHIRE

O N THE EDGE of Essex, Bishop's Stortford provided DANIEL WARNER and JOHN SANDERS. Warner, a carpenter in a family of carpenters,[71] surveyed the congregational chapel at Stansted in 1780, producing a plan[72] of the building and school. In 1783 he surveyed[73] parcels of land (48 a.) and the buildings, including a soap factory, belonging to Sam Day. The surveys are known from copied maps. Warner styled himself "surveyor" and he was obviously more a carpenter who surveyed buildings than a surveyor of lands.

In 1779–80 John Sanders made a written survey[74] of land in Hatfield Broad Oak that did not belong to the Barringtons. This survey has already been discussed with Mackoun's map of the Barrington land (see page 69). Like most other land surveyors, Sanders was concerned with land sale. His only other Essex survey[75] was made in 1788 of a small farm in Roxwell. The map has a plain clear script and a nice vase with tulip chain for the cartouche. A pleasing touch is the well drawn three-armed sign post at a road junction. Sanders' other work was confined to Hertfordshire.[76]

Early in his career, GEORGE COLE surveyed[77] the whole parish of Sible Hedingham. This was in 1797 and he was back in 1810 to survey the whole parish of Great Waltham. Parish surveys, initiated by the parish council, were becoming popular during the last years of the 18th century. It is surprising that Sible Hedingham should have been surveyed by Cole, who came from Aylesbury. For at that time two nearby Essex surveyors were concerned with whole parish surveys. They were le Neve of Ardleigh and Cole of Colchester.

A bad map[78] of a small Epping farm was called "an accurate survey" in 1800 by J. Moore of Hoddesdon. This was made at the end of his career of surveying mainly in Hertfordshire and Berkshire.

FROM NORTH OF ESSEX

S AMUEL LEWIS, OF East Bergholt, lived so close to the Essex border that his excursions into North Essex were to be expected. In 1769 he surveyed the Glebe at Langham[79] and a farm in Lawford.[80] Of interest to students of cartography were his surveys[81] in Dedham of a wood (1771) and a mill (1774) both of which had belonged to Thomas Seckford of Woodbridge, Suffolk, the patron of Christopher Saxton. These maps were used in a Chancery Court dispute (Rolfe v. Baron) over the Seckford estate. Lewis continued his "bits and pieces" surveying with farms in Stanway[82] (1774) and Birch[83] (1784). In Lexden he surveyed[84] a total of 614 acres of farmland belonging to Mrs Ann Rawstorn (1781 and 1789).

Lewis was appointed surveyor for the enclosure of Navestock Heath in 1770. The public notice of the enclosure (in the *Chelmsford Chronicle*) stated that "Samuel Lewis the surveyor . . . with his assistants will attend on the 23rd and 24th of March in order to show the several allotments staked out" and that Lewis would stay in Navestock Hall. His map[85] of the enclosure is plain with a cumbersome roman script.

Lewis married in 1774 Sarah Folkard, also of East Bergholt, whose brother was a carpenter.[86] The sale of Black Notley Hall in 1773 was advertised by a John Lewis of East

Bergholt who may well have been a relative of Samuel's. Samuel had a long career, mostly working in Suffolk, but in 1802 made a map ("Samuel Lewis Delint.") of Blake Hall near Ongar.

William Jennens of Acton Place, Suffolk, had his Essex farm at Bulmer surveyed in October 1794 by JOHN KINGSBURY, "Land Surveyor, Melford". The map[87] is very pleasing with a nice achievement of the Jennens' arms, good scripts and a delightful cartouche of ears of wheat, barley and oats. Kingsbury used an almost identical cartouche for his 1796 map[88] of Ardleigh Hall (337 a.) on which he painted a water colour picture of the Hall and its outbuildings.

ISAAC JOHNSON (1734–1835) lived in Woodbridge and, like his father John, achieved a considerable reputation as a land surveyor. The whole family, of artists and surveyors, were Nonconformists and their history has been recorded by Blatchley and Eden.[89]

Isaac Johnson's Essex work is notable for the large size of the estates he surveyed and the fact that the land owners concerned mostly had estates in Suffolk as well. In 1784 he surveyed the Essex estate of W. B. Rush. The maps[90] were drawn on the pages of a soft-cover book and have a neat minimum of Adamesque decoration. No doubt this book of maps was taken from large scale sheet maps in the first place. The notable feature of the book is that the last page has a map of a farm in Great Braxted drawn by Matthew Hall from his survey "taken Jan. 1789". Johnson made another set of maps[91] "contracted from the original plans" which he put in a hard-cover book and dated 1792. The title is set in a sylvan scene, well painted in water colour. It is interesting that he copied Hall's map.

There is also an undated anonymous book of maps[92] by an amateurish hand, which records Rush's Essex estates (copying Johnson) and also his Suffolk estate, presumably originally surveyed by Johnson.

Johnson surveyed the 3304 acre Stoke College estate in north Essex and south Suffolk. The decorated map[93] of the estate (surveyed and planned in 1791 and 1793) has fine clear scripts, a cartouche of flower chains topped by an urn, and a remarkable compass rose of intricate pattern drawn in black ink. The layout of the "working surface" is encumbered by the number of outlying parcels of land that had to be squeezed together. There is also a "rough plan"[94] of the estate and another version by Johnson dated 1797.

In 1797 Johnson surveyed[95] the 3204 acre estate of Baroness Lucas. Most of the land, centred on Brewards Hall, was in the parish of Great Horkesley, but the estate extended into south Suffolk. Johnson's one small Essex survey[96] was of a small farm in Great Holland, probably made at the end of the century.

In the early 19th century Johnson joined in the new fashion for Essex parish maps, surveying[97] the parish of Gestingthorpe in 1804 (his map was the basis for the 1838 tithe map) and Barking parish in 1805.

Isaac Johnson had a further Essex connection in that his brother William, artist and drawing master, lived in Chelmsford and died there in 1797.

THOMAS WARREN Jnr., of Bury St Edmunds, who with his father made many Suffolk surveys, visited Essex for two large commissions from wealthy land owners. In 1774 he surveyed almost the whole parish of Great Chesterfield for the Earl of Bristol. The map[98] is clear but plain; the buildings are shown in elevation "laid on their backs" by the roadside to give an old fashioned look to the map. Like his relative, Francis Warren, before him, he surveyed 900 acres of Audley End in 1783. The map[99] is elegant with a light rococo cartouche and fine black ink drawing to show the estate from a "bird's eye" view, particularly the hedgerow trees, distinguishing deciduous from coniferous. The gardens of Audley End are shown in plan but there are good drawings in elevation of the mansion and a classical temple.

FROM FAR AFIELD

BENJAMIN PRYCE, from Dorset, surveyed for Charterhouse in the Essex parishes of Southminster and Cold Norton in 1775–6. His large survey of Southminster in 1775 was of "farms belonging to Suttons Hospital founded in Charterhouse . . . by Benjn. Pryce of Dorchester". He showed all the separated farms (2340 acres in total) on one map[100] in a pattern of lands and reference tables. He also made a series of eight maps[101] showing, with more clarity and elegance, the individual farms. The large map has a simple cartouche of an oval leaf and bud chain, the small maps having no cartouche. These maps are distinguished by a clean black-on-white appearance with beautiful clear scripts and neat field boundaries. Pryce was almost ahead of his time with precise simplicity of map design that was more popular towards the end of the century. His 1776 survey, probably made during one prolonged stay in Essex, was of Norton Hall farm in Cold Norton. Again the map[102] shows the same clear scripts and the title decorated with serifs. Buildings are drawn in block plan but the church is well shown in perspective. The farm was large, 668 acres in all; "about 60 acres of the said quantity is of but little profit to the tenant".

From 1769 to 1798 Pryce made many surveys[103] in Dorset, several in conjunction with William Corfield of Salisbury, where Pryce lived when he left Dorchester. Pryce also surveyed in Wiltshire, where Charterhouse had estates. But Pryce was employed by Charterhouse only for the Essex surveys.

Two outsiders came to Essex in 1778. BENJAMIN CHAMBERS surveyed Gosling's Hassobury estate (bought by him in 1773) lying in Farnham and Manuden. The map,[104] like Pryce's work, has a clear clean appearance due to good scripts. Chambers lived in Derbyshire and surveyed in that county. Later he became a cotton mill engineer in Yorkshire, which may explain why Gosling did not ask him back for later surveys; they were carried out by William Smith.

BENJAMIN ARMITAGE surveyed the manors of Mark Hall and Latton Hall in the parish of Latton (1750 acres in all). This was done for the owner, William Lushington, who later sold the estate to Montague Burgoyne, a politician under the wing of Lord North. The map[105] is undecorated and may well be a draft or a copy of the finished map. Apart from this map, Armitage's career is associated only with Yorkshire.

Another Yorkshireman, WILLIAM FAIRBANK, surveyed the 150 acres of Broxted farmland owned by Thomas Leader. The Fairbank family[106] were Quakers who lived in Sheffield. The Fairbank of this 1779 Broxted survey was William II, his father being William I who was a schoolmaster surveyor. William II was also a schoolmaster who surveyed, but he became a full-time surveyor in 1774. His brother Joseph was also a surveyor. William II (1730–1801), had a son, William III, who became a surveyor. To complicate matters Joseph also had a son called William (IV) who surveyed. All were town and country surveyors.

From the historian's point of view, the Fairbank family was unique in that all their surveyor's notebooks were kept and now form the Fairbank collection in the Sheffield City Library. The notebooks of William II contain all his measurements made in Broxted, and there is a draft map there to go with the finished map[107], which is well drawn with a light classical cartouche of twin pillars at the side joined by rococo moulding and surmounted by a pagoda-like design. The records also make it clear as to why William II should have made such a long journey from Sheffield to Broxted. In Sheffield he had surveyed the workshops of Tudor, Leader and Nicholson, manufacturers of silver and plated goods. The Leader family were prominent in Sheffield, and most likely Thomas Leader of Broxted was a relative. His notebook shows that Fairbank went on from Broxted to survey the estate of William Forster in Tottenham, Middlesex. As Fairbank had married Mary, the daughter of Josiah Forster, a Quaker and a surveyor of Tottenham, it is likely that the survey was for one of his wife's relations.

In his will Fairbank left to his son the "instruments used for the land surveying", an unusual bequest among 18th century surveyors but common in the wills of the few Elizabethan gentlemen who practised surveying.

WILLIAM YATES of Liverpool, known best for his large scale county surveys, surveyed the Bamber-Gascoyne estate in 1794. The bulk of the land was in Lancashire (brought to the family by the marriage of Mary Greene to Bamber-Gascoyne in 1756) but Yates completed the survey by coming down to view the land in Barking, Dagenham and Hornchurch. Yates was assisted in his Essex work by a local surveyor, John Hindley. The original maps by Yates are now unknown but all were copied in Yates' office in 1799. The copies[108] were bound into a book with a splendid title page painted by George Yates, William's son. "Maps of the Estates belonging to Bamber Gascoyne 1799" is written on an oval surrounded by a wild woodland scene, a most romantic interpretation.

There are 10 maps of the Lancashire lands and six of the Essex property. From Hindley's commentary of 1804, Yates measured lands in Barking and Dagenham shown in three maps and viewed the other lands using old maps which he drew again in three maps. This practice of land surveying with the use of old maps, rather than a complete remeasurement, was probably quite common. Certainly Scalé did that in Stifford and Storer did so in High Ongar, adding to Rocque's map.

Essex Surveyors

NORTH ESSEX

JOHN STORER of Halstead continued his long and busy career up to the end of the century. Two sons of surveyors made brief appearances. JOHN AGNIS, son of Benjamin Agnis and inheritor of his Colchester farm, surveyed[109] Bradley Hall in Ardleigh in 1773. THOMAS ALEFOUNDER junior of Nayland surveyed[110] 46 acres in Boxted (1781) for Sadler of Great Horkesley, who later used William Cole as a surveyor. Alefounder also advertised land for sale in 1783.

In 1776 WILLIAM BEAUCHAMP of Earls Colne publicly thanked[111] those who had employed him in surveying and mapping their estates and declared that he measured land "by the latest improved methods" and would copy maps on any scale. No example of his work is known. Storer in nearby Halstead must have been stiff competition. By contrast it is not known where THOMAS NICHOLSON lived but there is just one map[112] by him, made in 1777, of his survey of Richard Muilman Trench Chiswell's estate, which he gained in 1772 by marriage to Mary Trench. The estate covered the whole parish of Debden and extended in to Thaxted, Wimbish and Widdington. The map is remarkable for its size (8' by 6' 7", mounted on a roller) and for its working surface drawn entirely in black ink, even the trees. However the decorations are painted in many bright colours. Unusual for a map of this date, there is a highly decorated broad border of trees and individual flowers. The title is set between two large trees and on the well painted ground between their trunks are scattered various agricultural tools. The contrast between the spare black line of the fields and the lavish decoration hints that someone other than Nicholson did the decorations. Nothing else is known of Nicholson. The Muilmans seemed to have chosen surveyors known only from one map. Richard's father chose R. Dyer in 1766 to survey the Little Yeldham estate and nothing else is known of him.

RICHARD WENHAM called himself a land surveyor but he also ran a school that taught surveying[113] in Wivenhoe, perhaps the same school where in 1734 Hayward Rush was teaching navigation. Wenham's surviving work is confined to two undistinguished maps, one of 19 acres in Frating[114] (1772) and the other of 21 acres in Brightlingsea[115] (1774).

The best known schoolmaster and the leading Colchester surveyor was WILLIAM COLE. When he died in 1824, aged 87 years, the *Ipswich Journal* lauded him as "one of the ablest land-surveyors of the day. His shining talents in the mathematics and music are well known to the public. In the latter his compositions are so eminent as to render his name immortal, and his friendly disposition . . . will long make his remembrance pleasing to a numerous acquaintance." It is his maps, not his music, that survive.

Cole came from an Ipswich Nonconformist family, and in 1765 he was appointed master of the Independent Charity School in Moor Lane (now Priory Street) Colchester.[116] A year later an advertisement[117] with the title "Land-surveying by W. Cole and J. Dunthorne" stated that the pair, "having considered the Disadvantages that often attend the Business of Surveying when carried out by one person only, intended jointly to carry on the said business, and by each attending to that Part of it which is particularly adapted to his profession, they flatter themselves that they will be able to produce Plans that are (both in point of Accuracy and Elegance) inferior to none. N.B. Perspective Views of particular places will be inserted at the Head of the Plans if desired."

Cole, "amongst his other acquirements, had learnt the art of surveying land and buildings". He was known as "a remarkably good mathematician, the most ingenious man" who used Hadley's sextant.[118] James Dunthorne was a Colchester artist ("limner") who had been trained by Joshua Kirby, an Ipswich artist who also made several Suffolk estate maps and was a friend of Thomas Gainsborough.

The partnership never blossomed. An undated map of a small estate with "Actually surveyed by Wm. Cole. Dunthorne Delint." may have been produced soon after the announcement of partnership. However a map of Copford Place, with a perspective drawing of the house, and "Surveyed by W. Cole. J. Dunthorne Delint." is dated 1810. This only dated example of their work comes 34 years after their declaration of working together. By that time Cole was aged 73 years but still an active surveyor, measuring the whole parish of Great Tey and going the bounds with the parish officers. Indeed Cole must have held the 18th century Essex record for oldest working land measurer.

An added problem is that 1780 is the first date to be found on Cole's maps. It may be that his teaching duties prevented him from surveying. At the end of the century when he was a busy surveyor Cole "took no part in teaching the boys, nor did he often come into the class-room".[119] Yet he did not retire from the school until 1807.

It is more likely that some of Cole's early work has been lost and that some of his undated maps were made before 1780. For in 1781 he returned thanks[120] to those who had employed him as a land surveyor and announced that he "continues to survey gentlemen's estates etc. and delineate maps of the same", without reference to Dunthorne. In that year Cole was joint surveyor with Blyth of a farm belonging to James Round. As Round had used Blyth as a surveyor in 1775, it looks as if Blyth introduced Cole to Round as a steady client.

Illustration, page 8

Cole's style of cartography was very personal and never changed throughout his long career. His maps are attractive in their artistic blending of "working surface", scripts and decoration. Most of his cartouches form a light rococo framework for the title and he made

Illustration, page 119

much use of Adamesque swags and chains of flowers, especially around contents tables. His trademark was a pendant decoration below the scale bar. The overall style belonged more to the middle of the 18th century than to its closing years. It is possible that Cole's style derived from Dunthorne's teaching. However the Blyth-Cole map is of the same style and Blyth had used the pendant scale bar decoration in 1756. The only other surveyor to use it was Plume of Lexden in 1797. It is conceivable that Dunthorne, as a Colchester artist, taught all three Colchester surveyors the art of cartography.

There are several interesting features in Cole's surveys. For instance, there are an unusually large number of maps of small farms (less than 90 acres). James Round contributed to this by his habit of getting his lands surveyed in bits and pieces, using Blyth, then Cole and even Hutson up from Hutton. Up to 1790 Cole's only major work was the survey of the Tendring marshes for the Commissioners of Sewers. The four maps (1783) illustrate all the characteristics of Cole's cartography. They are also the only maps that Cole made for an institution.

Although small surveys continued after 1790 there were more surveys of much bigger areas further away from Colchester, notably his work at Burnham for Lady Mildmay. His survey at Great Braxted for Malkin in 1798 may give a date for an undated map of 21 acres in nearby Wickham Bishops for Du Cane. This map is headed "Plan IX" so it must have been part of a larger work. Du Cane himself wrote on the plan "this map is not accurate" as it omitted two parcels of land. It is possible that Cole was not the surveyor and was just copying old plans when he erred in transcription, not measurement.

By far the most major commission from a private land owner came to Cole in 1796 when he surveyed the 2160 acre Rochford estate belonging to Tylney Long. Cole produced an elegant volume of 16 maps, preceded by a written account of the estate. The drawing of every map is most elegant and in Cole's usual style. His polar indicators are simple lines, he never decorated them. Most of the cartouches are rococo but the title of two maps is displayed on a torn-paper effect as used by Scalé. As pure speculation, did Cole ever see Scalé's work for Rigby? Certainly Cole was trying to produce a volume of similar beauty, "actually surveyed and drawn by W. Cole". The result showed Cole to have been a surveyor and cartographer of the highest rank, by far the best of the many Essex schoolmasters turned surveyor. An interesting point is that while Cole was working in Rochford, Tylney Long had the Londoners, Mumford and Doyley, surveying his estates in Felsted.

At the turn of the century Cole cashed in on the new demand for parish maps. But he had proved himself in this field back in 1790, when he surveyed the parish of Southminster. For this he produced a well bound book with a long written description of the parish and 11 maps. In fact he produced two identical books, one going to the parish authorities, the other to the Governors of Charterhouse, the major land owner in the parish. As Cole explained, ". . . a part of the survey, comprehending the farms belonging to Sutton's Hospital called the Charterhouse, was taken in the year 1775 by Mr B. Pryce of Dorchester from whose plans these farms are copied into the annexed maps". It was also in 1790 that the Governors of Charterhouse decided to buy the 1777 Chapman and André maps of Essex. They added a note to these maps,[121] "Mr Cole of Colchester having made a survey of the parish of Southminster discovered various mistakes in the laying down (Plate XIX) of some of the principle farms in the marshes." There were not many who caught out Chapman.

Cole's next parish survey, in 1794, was a relatively minor affair, showing the parish of All Saints, Colchester, for which he was paid only 10 guineas. Other parish surveys, notably of Great Tey and Great Horkesley, came early in the 19th century. Correspondence[122] suggests that he also surveyed Little Horkesley and Lawford around 1800.

In 1793 Cole's daughter Elizabeth married Robert Hale, a Colchester baker. Under Cole's presumed tuition Hale emerged as a land surveyor by 1809. In 1817 "Messrs Cole and Hale, surveyors, Colchester" mapped the parish of Great Waltham. By that time the very aged Cole could have been no more than a sleeping partner in the enterprise. Later Hale continued a successful career in surveying.

Cole and Storer, the only two north Essex land surveyors listed as such in the *Universal Directory*, had very different careers. Cole stuck to land measurement and mapping, Storer was more concerned with land sale, estate supervision and auctions. However both became secretaries of their local association against felons, the land owner's insurance. It is significant that Cole mapped the parish of Great Tey but Wiggins, the surveyor-estate supervisor from Danbury, was called in to set the tithes. However inactive in his duties, Cole continued as a schoolmaster, compared with Robert Baker of Terling who gave up his school to become, with his son, a full-time land surveyor, estate agent and adviser on agriculture.

TABLE TWELVE
THE MAPS OF WILLIAM COLE TO 1800

Date	Parish	Comment	Reference
(undated)	Brightlingsea	Surveyed Cole 85 a. farm Dunthorne Delint.	D/DDw P50
1780	Fingringhoe	88 a. farm	D/DEl P77
1780	Great Clacton	36 a. farm called Smythies	Institute of Chartered Surveyors
(undated)	" "	56 a. farm of Mr F. Smythies Anon. ?by Cole	C/TS 46
1781	Birch	By Blyth & Cole. 114 a. farm for Round	D/DR P12
1782	West Mersea	81 a. farm	D/Q 1/27
1783	Tendring	4 maps of marshes for Com. of Sewers	D/ST 17–20
1784	Stanway	47 a. farm for Round	D/DEl P17
1785	Birch	135 a. farm for Round	D/DEl P18
"	Great Bromley	63 a. Plan of farm buildings	D/DHt P24
1786	Mount Bures	small parcels of land	T/M 497
1787	Colchester	12 a. for Phillips	D/DU 728/5
(undated)	Lexden	6 a. for Phillips (?by Cole)	D/DU 728
1788	Peldon	80 a. farm	D/DHt P26
1790	Colchester	36 a. farm for Round	D/DR P13
(undated)	" "	24 a. farm for Round (? by Cole)	D/DEl P20
1790	Birch	216 a. farm for Round	D/DEl P19
"	Little Horkesley	97 a. farm	D/DOt P4
"	Kelvedon	147 a. farm	D/DWe P6
"	Southminster	11 maps of whole parish and manor of Southminster Hall	D/P 259/28 Also in GLC Rec. Off.
1792	Wethersfield	29 a. farm	D/DHt P43
1793	Marks Tey	31 a. farm	T/M 381
"	Great Horkesley	77 a. farm	D/DHw P6
1794	Burnham	817 a. farm for Mildmay	D/DM P9
"	Steeple	227 a. farm for Shaw King	D/DQh 4
"	Colchester	Parish of All Saints (book of 3 maps)	D/DHt P60
1796	Great Horkesley	191 a. farm for Rev. Sadler (?by Cole)	D/DEl P21
(undated)	W. Bergholt	57 a. farm for Sadler (?by Cole)	D/DEl T259
1796	Rochford	Rochford Hall estate (2160 a.) shown on 16 maps	D/DCw P13
1798	Little Oakley	637 a. for Sir Wm. Rowley	D/DRw P1
" "	Parndon	small farm	D/DCw P14
" "	Great Braxted	227 a. farm	D/DU 19/12
circa 1800	Wickham Bishops	21 a. for Du Cane	D/DDC P4
"	" "	8 a. of heath	D/DEl P67
"	Stanway	part of farm with doubtful boundary	D/DEl P26
1800	Colchester	112 a. farm	D/DEl P76
"	Kirby	400 a. farm	D/DQh 5
"	Birch	608 a. for Round (2 maps)	D/DEl P22 & 24

Note. Maps noted as ?by Cole are anonymous but clearly in Cole's style. At least two other anonymous maps may be of Cole's surveys. D/DEl P42 is dated 1783 and shows a farm of Round's in Felsted. D/DB P39 is undated and shows a farm in Ardleigh belonging to F. Smythies (see Cole's undated map of Great Clacton and in the same parish "a farm called Smythies", 1780.)

EDMUND PLUME was a Lexden farmer but in 1797 he mapped[123] 39 acres in that parish belonging to Isaac Green, a prominent Colchester builder who also styled himself surveyor when advertising a house for sale. Surveyor, in his case, obviously meant "of buildings" and not "of land". Plume's drawings of buildings on his map are of poor quality but the pendant decoration under the scale is very similar to that used by Blyth and always by Cole. It has already been noted that the three surveyors may have learnt this decoration from Dunthorne the painter. Plume did have artistic friends as another Colchester painter, Briggs, often stayed with him in Lexden.

PETER LE NEVE lived in Ardleigh and styled himself "land surveyor". He bore the name of a well-known Norfolk antiquarian and herald (1661–1729) but no direct family link is known. Le Neve's first maps were neat unembellished sketches (some titled "A rough map of . . .") of 73 scattered acres in High Roothing[124] (1786), of only 19 acres in Ardleigh[125] (1790), of a 100 acre estate in Broomfield[126] (1791) and a parcel of land in Frating[127] (1792). An undated map[128] of two farms in Ardleigh belonging to Lady Aflick probably comes from this period. Some of this scanty surviving work was done away from Ardleigh and the survivors may indicate a larger output of local surveys.

By 1794 Le Neve was well enough known to survey 591 acres in Barling,[129] making "A plan of that Part of the Parish of Barling which is not the property of the Dean and Chapter of St Pauls, London, being a supplement of the Plan of their Demesne lands taken by Samuel Williams in 1766 to the whole Parish excepting about 40 acres of Saltings lying within the Sea Wall and of Very Inferior Value." The "working surface" of this map is rather untidy with blurred boundaries, numbered fields but no table of contents. However a heavily gilded "mirror-frame" encloses a nicely scripted title, and two beautifully painted sprays of moss roses reach out from the frame. The map also shows two of Le Neve's personal cartographic characteristics, a scale of chains "per Gunter" and a polar indicator formed of four lozenge shapes. Another decorative map,[130] dated 1796 (of 51 a. in Lawford) has the title displayed on a pedestal bearing an urn and Le Neve's name written on a rock with a seated man and a distant view of Lawford Place. This sort of sylvan scene was depicted by many cartographers from 1780 to the end of the century.

In 1797 he made a major survey of 873 acres in Great Bentley, shown in three maps, which are now known only from later copies.[131] With these larger commissions Le Neve started to advertise[132] land for sale and had obviously settled down in the role of a local land surveyor. In 1798 he surveyed the whole parish of Ardleigh. The map, now unknown, must have been a good one for in that year the parish clerk announced[133] that "The parish of Ardleigh, near Colchester, has been accurately measured and a MAP delineated, the same as a single estate, by Mr Peter Le Neve, land surveyor at Ardleigh. Ardleigh is supposed to be the largest parish in Essex, Writtle excepted. The map affords great variety, on account of several woods, groves and small commons being interspersed; it is also intersected by a great many roads and watercourses . . . The map contains 42 square feet. It may be seen by way of a specimen of the ability of the surveyor by applying to me, M. Lugar." This testimonial may have prompted the parish council of East Ham to have their parish surveyed by Le Neve in 1800. The resulting map is a disappointing draft.[134]

Le Neve lived modestly in Ardleigh; the Land Tax returns record him as an "outdweller" and his property attracted the minimum tax for the parish. He continued to work until 1820, never surveying outside Essex but busy enough near to his home.

Well west of Colchester, Saffron Walden produced two interesting characters. Unravelling the story of ATKINSON FRANCIS GIBSON required some detective work. His only map,[135] dated 1786, was of just 18 acres in Hatfield Peverel. An early 19th century survey of this land by Baker indicated that most of the parcel belonged to "The Trustees of the Witham Monthly Meeting for the use of Poor Friends". The map itself is strikingly professional in its neat outlines and script like a good typeface. The reason for this was made clear by an advertisement[136] published in April 1785: "A. F. Gibson, land surveyor, Saffron Walden, after having served a regular Apprenticeship with a person of eminence in that profession" solicited work, with orders to be "executed with despatch and in the neatest and most accurate manner". To whom was he apprenticed?

Thanks to a family tree compiled by his descendants,[137] it is possible to identify the young surveyor as a Quaker, born in Saffron Walden, the son of George Gibson, who had come from Maldon, and a Yorkshire girl. The key document is a letter[138] dated February 1785 (two months before Gibson announced himself as a land surveyor) from the Friends of Balby Monthly Meeting, Yorkshire, to the Friends of Thaxted Monthly Meeting, Essex. The letter reads "Dear Friends, we apprehend it necessary on Atkinson Francis Gibson' return from us to settle among you, to certify that during his residence here his conduct was commendable and orderly. We esteem him as a Member in unity with us and know not but he left us free of debt and Engagements respecting Marriage." Among the many signatories are William Fairbank and William Fairbank Jnr, two generations of the great Sheffield family of Quaker surveyors. Thus, the letter must have been written when Gibson had completed his apprenticeship with Fairbank and had returned to Saffron Walden to set up as his own master.

Apart from the map of 1786, there is no record of Gibson's surveying and no mention of his being a surveyor in the family tree. If his father, who must have been in Maldon when Fallowes the Quaker surveyor was ending his career, had wanted a Quaker master for his son he might well have chosen the Drivers of Old Kent Road. Presumably it was the mother's Yorkshire connections that arranged an apprenticeship in Sheffield.

An attractive interwoven border to a cartouche by Matthew Hall Jnr. (see p. 120), 1777 (see illus. p. 90)

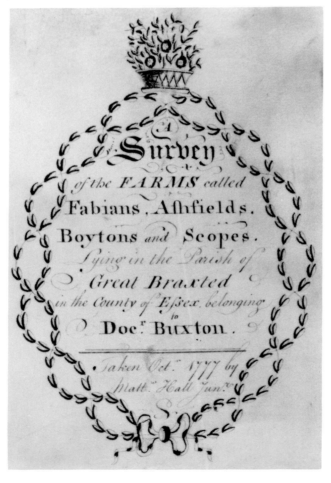

In 1789 Gibson married Elizabeth Wyatt, a Quaker of Saffron Walden, the daughter of a "common brewer". It would appear that Gibson took up her family's business as he later signed documents[139] as a "common brewer". He certainly prospered, for by 1795 he owned property in the High Street and in quaintly named Cuckingstool End, Saffron Walden.[140] Gibson had five children, all of whom did well, and died in 1829, being buried in the Friend's burial ground at Saffron Walden.

The other Saffron Walden surveyor was MARTIN NOCKOLDS. His father, also Martin, was nurseryman and then steward to Lord Howard at Audley End. The newspaper account[141] of his death in 1796 expressed the hope that his two sons would follow in his footsteps as he was much respected for his 30 years' work with Lord Howard. Surveying and estate management did become the career of the two sons and of other young Nockolds.

Nockolds' first surviving map[142] is dated 1794 but probably does not mark the beginning of his career for in that year he advertised[143] for an assistant "who understands land surveying and can plan with accuracy" and added that he, Martin

Nockolds junior, correctly surveyed, valued and mapped estates. Incidentally, the assistant did not stay long as Nockolds advertised again for an assistant in 1796.

Nockolds' 1794 survey was for Charles Smith and the three maps were bound into the large book of maps made by Skynner in 1749 which showed most of Smith's large estates. Nockolds surveyed some additions to the land held in Stapleford Tawney and Stanford Rivers. A year later he surveyed Moor Hall farm[144] (242 acres) in Harlow, mapped by Moore in 1777, and two small farms in Steeple Bumpstead.[145]

An undated but very major survey[146] of 1330 acres lying in Wendon Lofts, Elmdon and Chrishall must have been made after the death of his father, as Nockolds had discarded "junior" from his name, and before the death of the land owner, Hopes Wilkes. So the date lies between 1796 and 1803. The survey was shown in 15 maps bound in a handsome volume. They are good examples of Nockolds' "clean look" and much like modern maps. The scripts are clear and elegant, the cartouches simple, usually two curved branches held by a ribbon knot. The same simple elegance and clarity of presentation can be seen on Nockolds' 1794 maps for Smyth.

The volume of maps for Wilkes has an interesting note on the flyleaf to state that Wilkes inherited the property in 1787 on the death of his brother. The note is signed by "Mr Nockolds of Tring, Herts". There is no date to it but probably the Nockolds of Tring was Martin's son.

A written "Estimation of Colne Engayne"[147] was made in 1767 for the parish authorities by OWEN SWAN. His only surviving Essex map[148] (1771) is of gravel pits in Black Notley. The map's conventional rococo cartouche is supported by two pillars rising from a brick wall set on grass. The pillars enclose a simple scale bar. The suggestion that Swan was a local Essex surveyor is insecurely based on the fact that an Owen Swan of Braintree was a parish overseer concerned with the building of the workhouse in 1730 and might have been the surveyor's father. Owen Swan the surveyor is otherwise known from his work in Suffolk (1765 and 1775) and Hertfordshire (1768).[149]

In his many advertisements,[150] all of land to be sold by auction, SAMUEL HARVEY of Kelvedon styled himself "auctioneer". He appears to have gone against against the common trend for a land surveyor to turn auctioneer. His career from 1772 to 1785 is well documented but the chronology is disturbed by a 1752 map by a Samuel Harvey. The cartography of this is crude and does not resemble that of the later maps. Possibly it was by his father or it might have been a juvenile effort of a man who had to wait 20 years before becoming established.

TABLE THIRTEEN
THE MAPS BY SAMUEL HARVEY

Date	Parish	Comment	Reference
(1752	Braxted	21 acres only	D/DBs P3)
1772	Kelvedon	John Leapingwell's farm (134 a.)	D/DDw P4
1773	Birch	Three farms (212 a.)	D/DEl P11
1774	Bradwell	Bradwell Quay	D/DCm P24
1775	Mayland	147 a. farm (copy by Raine*)	D/DMa P9
1785	Stanway	Land (451 a.) of de Horne	D/DU 893/1

*(Jonathan Raine was a London surveyor who copied Harvey's map in 1778 for the Mildmay family)

Harvey's surveys were for a variety of clients over a confined area of Essex. His 1772 survey for John Leapingwell can be matched with his sale, a year later, of the late Thomas Leapingwell's house. His inaccurate Bradwell map depicts on the quay "the new erected building that is now in dispute", which was probably the reason for the map being made.

Harvey was also concerned with the management of the manor of Great Wigborough with Salcott, as shown in several documents[151] from 1772 to 1782. An example can be taken from the General Court Baron of the manor held in May, 1782. There Robert Mott, a "Carraway and Tazle gardiner" (sic) of Tolleshunt D'arcy, surrendered his lease to John Bullock, the Lord of the manor, "by the hands of Samuel Harvey instead of the Lord's steward". Thus Harvey, like Storer, was concerned with the leasing of manor land and perhaps with its valuation. In short Harvey seems to have been doing the work that would now be done by a chartered surveyor and provided an 18th century local model of what was to come.

It may be a matter of family interest that from 1789 to the end of the century a Robert Harvey was an auctioneer in Witham, mainly concerned with the sale of property.[152]

That the maker of a good map should remain anonymous is a matter of regret. The Guy's Hospital estate (3761 a.) was surveyed and mapped[153] in 1780. The map shows the whole of the estate and so is of considerable size. It is very well drawn and decorated with a grey cartouche of intricate rococo design and some pleasing ships afloat in Oakley creek. The area covers the whole of Beaumont-cum-Moze and much of Great Oakley. Land holdings are distinguished by a complex colour code for the field boundaries. The cartography is unlike that of any local surveyor and the map itself was never in the possession of Guy's Hospital as it finally came to the Essex Record Office from Colchester solicitors. It was probably commissioned by John Yeldham, the estate's agent, who enjoyed a great degree of autonomy. It may be relevant that Yeldham at that time had just relinquished care of the St. Thomas' Hospital estates in Parndon which had been taken over by Joseph Freeman, land surveyor, whose cartographic style was not unlike that of the anonymous maker of the Beaumont map.

There is also a teasingly anonymous pair of maps, both dated 1783, depicting a 237 a. farm near Wimbish. The unusual feature is that both maps are decorated and show the same land on the same scale. Both are by the same hand and finely executed, with excellent calligraphy.[155] One has Adamesque decoration for its cartouche, set on a grassy bank on which a rabbit gambols. It also shows the farm house in elevation, with a ground plan below. The other[144] has a cartouche with different Adam motifs.

CENTRAL ESSEX

AFTER SKYNNER DIED in Chelmsford in 1770, ROBERT DALLINGER of Witham offered himself as successor to the "late eminent land surveyor". Dallinger, a schoolmaster, had been advertising[157] his skills from 1768, always in the same terms. He would measure and plan estates from 200 to 1000 acres at sixpence an acre, would measure timber, standing and felled, and copy, repair or reduce old maps. There was nothing in his list about valuation of estates. He taught navigation, dialling, mensuration and "other parts of the mathematics" and "performed all kinds of writing". If all that was not enough, "all kinds of mathematical philosophical and optical instruments" could be had from him. Dallinger's advertisements gave a full prospectus of what a local schoolmaster-surveyor had to offer.

Dallinger had a short career as a surveyor, probably ended by death, as a Mr Dallinger, schoolmaster, was reported[158] as dying in Walton in June, 1775. However in 1773 he surveyed[159] two farms in Rivenhall for Mrs Ann Western and copied[160] an old map of the parish of Wethersfield for the Dean and Chapter of St Pauls. On this copy he drew a simple "frame" cartouche but his large compass star was drawn on a separate piece of paper that was then stuck on to the map. It is possible that the map which Dallinger copied was the 1741 survey by Skynner that showed the whole parish. When Christie auctioned the great tithe of Wethersfield in 1792, a plan of the parish was available, perhaps the one made by Dallinger.

In 1774 Dallinger surveyed[161] two farms in Writtle for Lady Falkland and a small farm in Witham[162] for Jacob Pattison. The fact that Pattison used Raven to survey a farm in 1778 suggests that Dallinger had died.

Dallinger's last map[163] (1775) was of only eight acres in Wickham Bishops. On this he used an unusual method for showing timber with an explanation that "the figures in the hedgerows denote the number of trees in each. OP stands for oak pollard and OT for oak timber." As befitted a man who could perform all kinds of writing Dallinger employed a variety of pleasing scripts on all his maps.

Another Witham figure was THOMAS FORT, who in 1782 thanked[164] his clients for giving him work and reminded them that he continued to survey and map "in a correct and elegant manner". He also painted signs, coaches and houses, would reduce, copy or repair old maps and would paint in oils coats of arms on vellum. Unfortunately no example of his multiple talents survives.

In Terling, Strutt, who had employed Skynner, did not take up Dallinger's offer. Instead J. RAVEN, himself of Terling, did a lot of work on the Strutt estate. In 1774 he surveyed a series of farms in Terling and Hatfield Peverel; six maps[165] cover farms varying in size from 13 to 75 acres and another map[166] (known only from a later copy) showed one farm of 450 acres. It is likely that Raven had much to do with the day to day problems of the Strutt estate, as he drew a small plan of five acres in the large book that records details of the estate at various dates. The Strutt accounts record payments to Raven from November 1774. These payments are in round sums of pounds or guineas which, do not suggest payment by item of work. In 1776 payments of £10 and £20 are recorded. The last payment is dated February 1778 for the sum of six guineas. Below this Strutt wrote "The above money was advanced to Raven for surveying the parish and other farms but he died before he had executed it and I have only the rough draft at Terling."[167]

Two other Raven maps survive, one[168] (1776) a sketch of 27 acres in Broomfield bought in that year by Mildmay from Strutt, the other[169] of 329 acres in St Lawrence for Jacob Pattison, who seems to have been unlucky with the health of the two surveyors of his choice.

Raven's decorations show him to have been an imaginative cartographer. He drew cherubs holding a banner on which the contents table was displayed. One of his polar indicators is a sun in splendour with the points of the compass marked on its rays. One cartouche is surmounted by Cupid, another by a squirrel. One title is displayed on a flag hanging from a flagpole set in a hill, another is framed between trees on a hillside. On this map he drew six ships, with a written explanation that ship number 3 was taking on ballast. He could also draw a classical rococo cartouche, full of flowers and leaves. All his work was fresh and surprising. His scripts were clear and well formed. In having to map an outlying field in a wrong position, he justified his decision by writing "A should join B, being laid in that position for want of room."

The year after Raven died there was an advertisement[170] of timber for sale and for offers to plough up some woodland. The advertisement was inserted by a Mr Raven, apothecary of Hatfield Peverel. It is odd that an apothecary should publish such an advertisement, especially one called Raven who lived so close to Terling.

In 1775 Terling Hall was mapped by JOHN CASE. The map[171] has carefully-drawn trees that were boundary marks, a

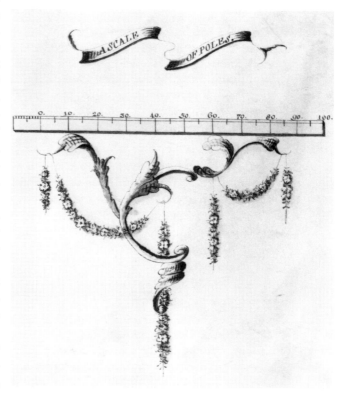

Scale bar by William Cole of Colchester (see p. 112), from a map of Tendring Level, 1783. The pendant decoration is a characteristic of Cole's maps.

119

classical cartouche but no scale bar and no polar indicator. This map (of 272 acres) can be related to the valuation[172] made in December of that year of the whole Terling Hall estate (about 7000 acres) "together with the number and value of the timber trees and pollards". The valuers were John Case, Edward Richardson (a surveyor from Hertfordshire) and Samuel Dowbiggin. Nothing more is known of John Case but at that time a dissenting minister, the Rev. Charles Case, was running a school at Witham.

Terling Hall estate was valued for its owner, Robert Cope, probably with the intent to sell, as the estate was bought by Strutt in the next year (1776). Strutt continued his land purchases in 1778 when he bought the manor of Little Baddow, being advised by JOHN WIGGINS of Danbury. Wiggins seems to have been the gentleman adviser on estates, rather like Wright of Woodham Mortimer (see page 22). He may have been a land measurer, as in 1787 he provided Strutt with detailed measurements[173] of land to be exchanged with Sir Brooke Bridges. Certainly his son, JOHN WIGGINS Junior, measured land and mapped. Young John just scraped in to the 18th century with his 1799 copy[174] for Charterhouse of Pryce's 1776 map of Cold Norton. The copy is so exact that it is difficult to tell the original from the copy. In the early 19th century young John pursued a busy career as a land surveyor in East Anglia and, like his father, advised on estates, in particular as superintendent of Lord Rochford's lands (1819).

Terling produced another surveyor in ROBERT BAKER. His trade card[175] is in the Strutt archive and written on its back is "On the Bill 1793 laid before Parl. Navigation, Chelmer and Blackwater". Strutt certainly objected to the Navigation Company's requests for portions of his land and he may well have retained Baker as a land measurer in case of dispute. The trade card itself states that "Robert Baker, at Terling near Witham, surveys plans and maps estates with Accuracy, Fidelity and Dispatch." At the bottom of the card are the words "Timber Measuring" and at the top "Youths boarded and educated on reasonable terms".

It is not known when Baker started his school but he was busy in Terling in 1792 as a collector of the Land Tax.[176] In 1794 he was advertising[177] as a land surveyor and schoolmaster, but a year later he was selling land as "Land surveyor &etc".

Baker's two surviving 18th century maps[178] are dated 1796. Both are of lands in Springfield, one a rough draft, the other with a fine clear script. On both he used a "stepped" scale bar, copied from Hutson and first used by Sangster, both surveyors from Brentwood.

By 1808 Baker had moved from Terling, presumably giving up his school, to Boreham, and continued as a land surveyor. His son, also Robert, joined him in the business and became a well known 19th century land surveyor, estate agent and expert on agriculture. He fulfilled his father's expectations in the business.

To the East of Terling, in Tolleshunt D'Arcy J. DAVEY owned a school where surveying was taught.[179] Davey also would survey, map and value estates, including timber. He would buy and sell land on commission. In the valuation and sale of land he differed from the usual schoolmaster surveyor like Dallinger. No trace of Davey's surveying can be found.

In Maldon MATTHEW HALL junior was yet another Essex surveyor from a Nonconformist family. His father, also Matthew, modestly described himself in his will[180] as a carpenter of Maldon, but by the time he died he had built up a considerable business as a timber merchant. As such he surveyed timber, measuring Strutt's timber in Terling in 1760 and making a neat plain plan of the woodland.

In April 1776 an advertisement[181] headed "Land Surveying" announced that Matthew Hall jun. surveyed and mapped by the most approved method "in a plain or embellished manner". Particular features such as hills and valleys would be "accurately delineated . . . by the rules of perspective" and that topographical plans would be truly copied. In practice his cartography conformed to the usual two dimensional cadastral map without representation of the relief of the land. He did draw buildings in elevation or perspective although most cartographers had long since discarded this method in favour of a block plan outline.

The April advertisement paid off with a flurry of work, starting in November with a survey[182] of Great Braxted glebe. The next year he was still in that parish working for Du Cane. He surveyed and mapped[183] the copyhold land occupied by Dr Buxton (172 a.), and then measured all Du Cane's freehold and other copyhold lands. These totalled 994 acres, recorded (1778) in a written account[184] without a map. He also surveyed and mapped[185] two of Du Cane's farms in Tollesbury. Previously (1773) Storer had come down from Halstead to survey in Tollesbury for Du Cane, but presumably the advent of a local surveyor made Du Cane dispense with his services.

For other clients Hall surveyed Latchingdon Hall[186] (562 a.), a farm[187] in Broomfield and remeasured some land in Maldon, previously mapped by Pritty in 1759. All this was in 1777 and in the next year he surveyed a farm[188] in Purleigh and a tiny farm[189] in Heybridge. In March 1780 he surveyed a farm[190] in Hockley, styling himself as usual as "Matthew Hall Junior" but in that October his father died. In taking over his father's thriving timber business Hall could not devote much time to surveying, especially as his brother was not concerned, being an upholsterer working in London.

In 1781 Hall married a Miss Bygraves, the daughter of a well to do Maldon farmer. The families were sufficiently prominent for the *Chelmsford Chronicle* to announce the wedding as a news item. Later, Hall sold his father-in-law timber and even a map of England.

Hall's maps are well drawn with clear neat scripts and the minimum of decoration apart from the cartouche. His standard design of cartouche was a light Adam type urn at the top with an oval of two chains criss-crossing each other. For his Tollesbury maps he adopted a wider more solid frame and on one of the two maps the frame contains a large shell and a medallion showing a ship.

Illustration, page 5

There are no surviving maps by Hall for the 1780s, indeed he may not have made any. His accounts[191] for the years 1786–96 do exist. Amongst the many items for carpentry and timber in all forms there are several records to show that he was still surveying, both land and buildings. Like his father, he measured Strutt's timber, "to 12 days self and man measuring timber standing in Woodham Hall estate with expenses . . . total £18-18-0". Other entries include the valuation of a building "burnt down at Bardfield" and "Surveying and making a valuation of three houses". There are several items of land measurement, for which he always charged fourpence an acre, compared with the going rate of sixpence. "Measuring several pieces of common meadow and one piece of woodland", and "Measuring two meadows at Maldon". A more specific entry was "To surveying Purleighs Barn Farm and taking account of the lands in tillage and altering the map £1-0-0. For the man . . . showing us the fields one shilling." At this time Hall was also advertising timber for sale and properties to let.

The start of the Chelmer and Blackwater Navigation gave Hall a fresh outlet as a land measurer, cartographer and timber merchant. The plan[192] of the Navigation from Beeleigh Mills to Collier Reach (1793) was "surveyed under the direction of John Rennie, Engineer, by Matthew Hall". In 1794 the Company's clerk wrote[193] about Beeleigh Mill "I ordered Mr Hall to copy the plan which I borrowed", but this was not enough as a year later he wrote to Hall "please draw a plan of Beeleigh Mill by Wednesday." These plans (anonymous) still exist. Josselyn, the official surveyor to the Company, used Hall as a valuer of buildings, including Beeleigh Mill for a fee of £16-16-0 and Heybridge Hall. But land measurement was Hall's main task, "Get Mr Hall to measure the lands so that a date can be fixed for Mr Josselyn's valuation." Right up to the end of 1799 Hall was working on the project, writing "Yesterday I measured two pieces of common land . . . I should have gone up to Hoe Hill to measure that meadow of Mr Pigott's this morning if the rain had not prevented me." Obviously he had forgotten his surveyor's umbrella, so essential to the protection of instruments. As a carpenter Hall also had his uses. "Mr Collis, carpenter, will build the bridge at Hoe Mill according to the plan and estimate of Mr Hall".

Hall's last map[194] was of the saltings at Foulness, surveyed by him in June 1799 at a charge of fourpence an acre. The saltings had just been drained, with new channels cut and secured by nearly 97,000 wood piles supplied by Hall.

Active to the end, Hall died in 1800.

The last land surveyors in this group are related to the area of Chelmsford. A map[195] of Cranham farm in Little Waltham, belonging to John Marridge, was "surveyed April 1798 by Messrs SORRELL and HURRELL". The map shows the state of cultivation by careful colouring and the title is framed by sheaves of corn. There is no scale bar, but the scale is recorded as 16 poles to an inch. There is also an undated "rough plan of Cranham Farm belonging to Rev. William Walford . . . as surveyed by R. Sorrell and M. Hurrell". This plan[196] differs from the decorated map in several measurements. Written on its back is "The old map of a farm called Cranhams sold by Mr Marriage to Mr Hall".

There is no other map by Sorrell and Hurrell, both names common in this part of Essex. It is most likely that they were locals with an interest in land measurement. Joseph Dawson's survey for Richard Hoare of Boreham in 1776 was "by order of Mr Hurrell".[197] In 1798 M. Hurrell senior was living in Boreham, as was M. Hurrell junior, who occupied land owned by Walford. A Robert Sorrell was living in Great Waltham and there are earlier (1776) records of a Richard Sorrell, yeoman, in Little Baddow, who joined the local association against felons. Several land surveyors became officials in these local associations.

To the south of Chelmsford, possibly in Ingatestone, was E. DUCKER, who in 1770 surveyed 41 acres of copyhold land in Fryerning[198] for Wadham College, Oxford. The College appears to have favoured local surveyors for smaller portions of land, as it possesses Dallinger's 1774 map of Lady Falkland's estate and had Hutson of Hutton to survey in Writtle in 1780.

Ducker's other known survey,[199] of 1773, was of a 288 acre farm in East Tilbury. The map is known from a copy made in 1801. The Fryerning map is plain with a curious upright script that is meant to be decorative.

The will[200] of an Ingatestone (next to Fryerning) man was signed in 1773 by an Edmund Ducker, perhaps the surveyor.

Well to the west of Chelmsford was WILLIAM MOORE of Chipping Ongar. Maps by William Moore date from 1761 to 1800. The key to this apparent longevity is in an advertisement[210] of 1773 in which William Moore of Chipping Ongar thanks patrons for their continued support after the death of his father and states that he will continue the carpentry and joinery business, would measure timber, "as it is a branch I have had great practice in", and would survey and map land. This father and son combination of carpentry, timber and surveying is much like that of Matthew Hall in Maldon.

There are two surviving maps by William Moore senior, one[202] of a 422 acre farm in Bobbingworth (1761), the other[203] of a 126 acre farm in Stondon Massey that belonged to the rector of Shelley, near Ongar. Both maps have titles written on a banner and a minimum of colour. The maps by Moore junior have no banners, a deal of colour and different scripts.

Moore, the son, made his first map[204] in 1774 of a little farm in South Weald. After that his work was almost confined to two clients. For John Westbrooke he surveyed in all about 900 acres, mapping farms in Ongar[205] in 1774–5 and the next year in Norton Mandeville.[206] Some of these maps are plain, others have a pleasing asymmetrical rococo design for the cartouche.

For John Luther of Doddinghurst Place Moore surveyed in all about 1700 acres, starting with farms in Doddinghurst and Writtle in 1776. The Doddinghurst land is shown on two maps[207] at a scale of 20 inches to a mile and also on four small maps (10″ by 7″) in a book.[208] The last map in the book is of the Writtle farm "reduced from a larger scale". The large scale version is missing.

In 1777 Moore surveyed a Harlow farm[209] (242 a.) and a year later was back on Luther's land in White Roding. The farm he measured was contiguous with one mapped by Sherwood in 1730. Moore cleverly cut his vellum to fit into the Sherwood one and so made one map[210] from two surveys of very different times.

Moore's only journey outside the environs of Ongar was in 1779 to survey Luther's farms in Blackmore,[211] Canewdon,[212] Willingale Spain,[213] Wickford[214] and, finally, in Rayleigh[215] (529 a.). The Wickford map has a cartouche with the title displayed on a long scroll hanging from a tree branch, quite unlike Moore's usual decoration.

Illustration, page 79

For a carpenter, Moore was very much the surveyor of lands rather than buildings. Warner of Bishop's Stortford was a carpenter who mainly surveyed buildings and Hall of Maldon was more a timber merchant than a carpenter and surveyed both buildings and land. Presumably, after 1779, Moore continued his carpentry for there were no more surveys until his last in 1800. A draft map[216] for Fane (who inherited the Luther estates) shows a farm in Kelvedon Hatch and was "surveyed 1800 by Will Moore".

Before leaving the western part of south Essex in this time period two anonymous maps should be mentioned. The map[219] of Chigwell manor (undated, circa 1775) has such fine penmanship that it looks as if it had been engraved. There are no decorations and none are needed with the beautiful clear drawing. The other map[203] is of Hopkins Dare's estate in Theydon Bois and Loughton (446 a.). The map is finely drawn and well coloured, a nice example of honest good work. Neither of these maps is in a style adopted by local surveyors of the time.

SOUTH ESSEX

GEORGE SANGSTER, latterly with his son, continued his Brentwood business as nurseryman and surveyor until 1794. During the years he acquired some interesting neighbours.

In 1774 Ireland's leading land surveyor, PETER BERNARD SCALÉ, settled nearby at Great Warley. Scalé's story has been told recently.[219] He was a Huguenot, born (1739) in London, whose father died five years later. He grew up under the wing of his uncle Peter, an ex-soldier who lived in Colchester. Scalé's widowed sister, Mary Ann, married in 1751 John Rocque, the best known Huguenot cartographer in London. Young Scalé went with Rocque to Dublin, where the latter lived from 1753 to 1756 making many important surveys. Scalé stayed on and in 1758 set up on his own, surveying land "after the manner of John Rocque, his brother-in-law, by whom he was instructed".

Scalé returned to England in 1765 to marry in Dedham a local girl, Henrietta Letch. The pair settled in Dublin, where Scalé continued to produce beautiful estate maps and town plans, notably of Waterford, and a revised version of Rocque's Dublin plans. He was fully occupied in all aspects of land surveying, valuing estates and negotiating their sale or lease. What prompted him to leave Dublin is obscure. Perhaps it was his wife's influence. At Warley he bought the modest property of Mangroves. It seems more than coincidence that the steward of the manor of Great Warley was a Joseph Letch. But Scalé did not abandon his Dublin business. He ensured its continuity by taking into partnership two of his ex-apprentices who maintained the Irish work. Scalé himself went back to survey in Ireland on several occasions.

Scalé's first English survey was made in the year that he moved to Warley. He surveyed the Baker-Holroyd estates in Sussex, with a lovely map of the main house and surrounding lands, and a plainer map of outlying farms, a distinction he used often for Irish estates. But much of his time was then taken up in the preparation of his *Hibernian Atlas*, published in London in 1776.

Scalé's major work in Essex was his 1778 survey of Rigby's estates, based on Mistley. A written summary[220] of acreage indicates that much of the Essex land had been surveyed in 1761 and 1775, with several changes in the acreage of contiguous farms as tenants' holdings were altered. Scalé surveyed and mapped the whole 6723 acres, with three assistants employed by Rigby.[221] The survey covered the manor of Mistley, and parts of the manors of

Bradfield, Thorp, Kirby, Walton and Dale Hall in Essex; the Suffolk manors of Old Hall, Nether Hall and Branton Hall were also surveyed.

The book of maps[222] that Scalé produced is a jewel in the crown of Georgian surveying. He was used to producing such books for Irish estates so that their English owners could excite the admiration and envy of their friends. Such a "coffee-table" production must have suited the flamboyant and venal personality of Rigby.

Illustration, page 87

The "working surface" of the maps is beautifully drawn and coloured so that the natural features of the land, arable, pasture and woodland, are immediately apparent. Graded depth of colour shows the relief of the land. Much detail is shown, from the stacked timber on Mistley quay to the rigging of the ships lying alongside. His scripts are clear and elegant, and, for the title, lavishly decorated with serifs. His "trademark" was the setting of contents tables on a piece of torn paper, a trompe l'oeil effect that really comes off. Another mark was the decoration of each polar indicator with tools and instruments used in farming, surveying, art and war.

The title page of the Mistley survey is framed by a classical draped female figure on one side and a tree with a shield lying near its roots on the other. The ground between is strewn with the impedimenta of art and war. The title itself is surrounded by a flourish of serifs, typical of Scalé's calligraphy.

Scalé was mapping during the fifteen years (1770–1785) when estate cartography reached its Georgian peak in artistry and competence. He balanced a well drawn informative "working surface" with elegant decoration. This wholeness of execution distinguished the work of Scalé and the best of his contemporaries. Earlier 18th century estate maps too often had one splendid item of decoration sitting forlornly next to a poorly drawn "working surface".

Scalé's style was copied faithfully by Sherrard, his pupil and later Dublin partner. It was echoed in the 1790s by Asser of Dartford, Kent, who was reputed to have been Scalé's apprentice. It might be expected that Scalé had learnt his style from his master, John Rocque. Certainly the "torn paper" effect is seen at its most dramatic on the title page of Rocque's 1757[223] maps of Maynooth, Ireland. The page is framed by a sheet of paper torn open to reveal a park and great house beyond. A seated female figure broods in the foreground. This design is completely unlike the style of Rocque's one estate map of Essex land, but was made when Scalé was still working for Rocque. In 1760 Rocque, then on his own, mapped some of the Carton estate near Dublin. These maps show little of the skill and style to be found in Scalé's maps of the same estate made in 1769. It is arguable that Rocque employed his assistant Scalé to decorate at least some of his maps, including the ones of Maynooth.[234]

The only other English survey by Scalé was made in 1780 of the 418 acre Stifford estate belonging to the Company of Embroiderers. The map[225] is a typical example of his cartography. The map was copied twice in the 19th century, both copyists failing to achieve the artistic integrity of the original.

It is odd that a land surveyor with such proven skill failed to gain a large number of commissions in England. His considerable Irish reputation seems to have gone unregarded. From the time that he arrived in England he was concerned with the buying and selling of land, often in association with attorneys, such as Gepp of Chelmsford and his friend Firmin of Dedham.[226] This may have been enough to provide a suitable income. But he was fit enough and willing to measure land as he went back to Ireland in 1782 to survey an estate in County Waterford. He also did what other local Essex surveyors did in joining the local association against felons (as a founding committee member). He was just in time, as within months his poultry house at Warley "was broke open and three ducks stolen, taken and carried away".

In 1786 Scalé's life was completely changed when his wife inherited a fortune in land and cash. He retired in the next year, moving to Baddow, where he established himself as a prominent member of the community. In 1824 he moved again, this time to Colchester, where he lived until his death in 1826.

In 1779–80 GEORGE HUTSON Junior settled in Hutton, the other side of Brentwood from Sangster's nursery. Previously Hutson had lived with his father, a tenant farmer of Hockley Farm, Rayleigh. In Hutton the young Hutson farmed land owned by Backhouse Carr,[227] whose Essex estate he surveyed in 1777.

The extraordinary similarity of Hutson's first map (1771) and Sangster's 1769 map has already been discussed. It looks as if Hutson had Sangster's map before him when he made his own, and the pair may have met at that time, before they became neighbours. Hutson continued to use on all his maps the "stepped" scale bar that he copied from Sangster, although Sangster abandoned this device. The one personal disaster on Hutson's map, repeated by him in 1773, was his awful drawing of nude figures holding a mantle on which the explanation of the map is recorded.

Hutson was busy surveying mainly south of the River Blackwater while Storer of Halstead surveyed in areas north of this river. Hutson's

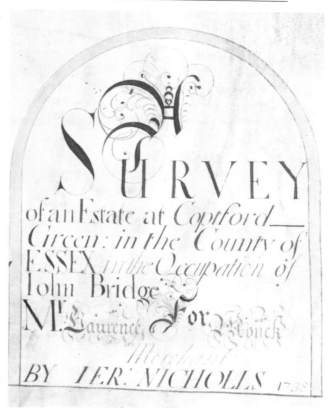

A crude cartouche by Jeremiah Nicholls (see p. 46), 1735. Its attempt to emulate the varied styles of lettering taught by the writing masters fails to disguise a less practised hand.

advertisement[228] of 1778 stated that estates were "carefully surveyed and neatly mapped either in sheets maps or in minature in books for the pocket". The number of scattered parcels of land that he was called upon to survey made books of maps very suitable, if somewhat bulky for a pocket. He managed to put on one map (1776) Richard Sorrell's 58 acre estate split over five parishes. He used a book of ten maps to show Robert Hust's 510 acre estate spread over eight separated parishes. This book has good clear scripts, light rococo decoration and a lot of topographical information. A page is devoted to the explanation of the symbols used, from styles and gates to "where the boundary line is jagged on the outside, the fencing don't belong to the estate."

His 1790 book of ten maps of Joseph Fraine's estate is of the same type, but with scripts more like typefaces and the decoration enlivened by little red flowers. This estate included land in Middlesex and its survey represents the only working journey that Hutson made outside Essex. An undated note book, with an outline of one field on each page, is not in Hutson's hand, however convenient for the pocket. It shows a farm in Little Baddow ". . . so far as it was ploughed. As it was surveyed by G. Hutson Jnr".

Of Hutson's single maps his 1777 Burnham survey for Lady Mildmay refers in the draft version to a 17th century map but makes no mention of John Lee's survey in 1728. Hutson also measured some Mildmay land, without mapping, at a charge of fourpence an acre. He, like Hall of Maldon, had an alternative source of income and so could undercut the usual local land surveyor's rate of sixpence.

Illustrations, pages 6 and 84

One commission from an institution came Hutson's way. In 1780 and 1788 he surveyed[229] the Wadham College (Oxford) estates that had been surveyed anonymously in 1737–42. His two excursions to north Essex are worthy of comment. His survey of the Manor of Stanway (689 a.) was later requested by Richard Woods, the landscape gardener, and the two met to discuss the matter. This meeting has been described in the section on Middleton, who provided the needed map. Hutson's survey of two farms in Copford (1792) is notable because the land belonged to James Round, who had used Cole of Colchester for many surveys. The switch in allegiance cannot be accounted for. Hutson's map (1791) of Springfield land (1791) belonging to Brosgrove of Springfield Place is accompanied by some land measurements recorded in a letter to him, "This is the written list of the several pieces of land which I imagine will answer your purpose 'till. . . you can have a plan of the whole."

Up to and including the year 1786 Hutson put "Junior" after his name on all his maps. The absence of "Junior" on subsequent maps strongly suggests that his father, also George, had died in 1787. However land tax returns for Rayleigh show that father George occupied his farm up to 1791; in the next year old George's household effects and his neat and genteel furniture were sold after his death and the farm's occupants became the Hutson family. The returns also show that "George Hutson Junior" became the tenant of some Rayleigh land in 1786, emphasising his role as a serious farmer.

Illustration, page 84

Hutson's cartographic style changed with the years, conforming to the conventions of the time. His earlier scripts, which included much Gothic lettering, inclined to more Roman letters akin to a typeface. His very early exuberance in cartouches was discarded in favour of a light rococo design which was often embellished with small flowers. He still had his more artistic moments such as writing the title of his 1789 map on a mantle held by an eagle, with a spray of red flowers below.

Throughout his career he dealt in land sales, in the manner of most local land surveyors. Farming, however, was always a serious business for him. He was active in business until March 1794. On the 14th of that month the *Chelmsford Chronicle* announced, "A few days since died suddenly Mr Hutson, land surveyor and farmer of Hutton; his ingenuity in planning and mapping stood unrivalled."

TABLE FOURTEEN

THE MAPS BY GEORGE HUTSON

Date	Parish	Comment	Reference
1771	Canvey	118 a. farm	D/DGe P14
1773	Little Baddow	100 a. farm	D/DQ 54/1
1775	Several	10 maps of R. Hust's estates (510 a.)	D/DU 23/137
1775?	Little Baddow	120 a. farm (in note book of fields)	D/DRa P10
1776	Baddow & nearby	58 a. of R. Sorrell's estate	D/DGe P20
1777	Burnham	173 a. for Mildmay (& draft – D/DGe P65)	D/DM P8
"	Several	estate of B. Carr	in private hands
1780	Writtle	172 a. farm for Wadham College	T/M 311
1783	Mundon	34 a. farm	D/DB P17
1786	Maldon	Maldon Hall 340 a.	D/DHt P25
1787	Great Baddow	113 a. for Tyrrell	D/DKe P1
"	Stanway	689 a. for Bellamy	T/M 283
1788	Writtle	464 a. farm for Wadham College	T/M 312
"	Canewdon	61 a. vicarage land	D/DU 743
1789	Mountnessing	20 a. farm	D/DP P36
1790	Several	1051 a. for J. Fraine (book of maps)	T/M 498
"	Great Waltham	127 a. vicarage land ("by G. H.")	D/DMa P13
1791	Fairstead	450 a. Fairstead Hall	D/DHt P54
"	Springfield	26 a. with letter from Hutson on other land measurement	D/DBo P1
1792	Copford	152 a. for Round	D/DZl 23

When George Sangster retired in 1794 he sold his business to JOSEPH GOLDING, who then announced[230] that, "having taken the Nursery at Brook Street", he sold "all sorts of trees shrubs plants and seeds at London prices", and added that, "having been also nine years with the late Mr Richard Woods", he surveyed estates with accuracy and mapped neatly. However there is now no evidence of his work at Brentwood. He only stayed in the business for three years. The land tax return for 1798 records Sangster as the land owner and the occupant as "Late Golding", indicating either death or departure.

Golding leads back to RICHARD WOODS, who in moving to Ingrave in 1783 became Sangster's neighbour. Woods described himself as a surveyor but in fact he was a landscape gardener. Time let Woods' contemporary reputation be eclipsed by the abiding distinction of "Capability" Brown. Fiona Cowell's recent detailed study[231] of Woods has restored him to his rightful place in the select band of great Georgian landscape gardeners.

Woods started his career when living at Chertsey and later he added a London business address. He designed parks and gardens for many distinguished land owners in many counties. His move to Essex in 1768 was a measure of his success, as he took on the tenancy of North Ockendon Hall, a considerable property belonging to Benyon of Gidea Hall. There he achieved a life style to which he had not been born.

Woods did only two straight estate surveys in his whole career. In 1767 he surveyed an estate in Berkshire but the map's decorations were by his assistant, James Ansell. Woods' other land survey[232] was of Rectory Farm (103 a.) at Bardfield Saling, Essex. The map is plain and poorly scripted. It was made in 1781 when his landscape commissions had become scarce. The style may be Woods' own, but, as Mrs Cowell pointed out, the variety of styles found on Wood's plans shows how many hands were involved. The plain Bardfield map contrasts with the lavish rococo embellishments of his plan for the improvement of Wivenhoe Park[233] (1765); this may have been more of Ansell's work.

The year 1783 was full of coincidences. 'Capability" Brown died and so did Mrs Woods. Humphrey Repton, having to economise, bought his cottage in Hare Street (eight miles from Ingrave) without a thought of becoming a landscape gardener. On his wife's death Woods sold up North Ockendon Hall, got married again and moved to a cottage in Ingrave, part of Lord Petre's estate. Petre appointed Woods as his surveyor at a salary of £100 a year.

Lord Petre had never employed Woods in his heyday. Instead his rival Brown worked on the grounds of Thorndon Park from 1769 to 1772 and Petre had Brown's own surveyor, John Spyers,[234] map the Park in 1778. But Woods was a Roman Catholic so it is probable that this prompted Petre to engage a co-religionist who was ageing and at the close of his career. Woods appears to have been concerned with the buildings rather than the land of the Petre estates. There is a letter of complaint from Woods to Lord Petre's steward concerning charges made for the Lodge, "it is a sad pick pocket business indeed" wrote Woods.[235]

It is of note that Petre had neglected the local talent in land surveying when much of his local estate was surveyed in the 1770s. But Woods is likely to have known or even instructed Henry Clayton, who, based at Ingatestone, started a successful career as a land surveyor in the early 1800s with surveys for Lord Petre. However there is no hint of Woods meeting Repton, who suddenly decided in 1788 to become a landscape gardener, despite no training. The wide difference in social class would have precluded such a meeting. Instead Repton contacted Brown's son and obtained from him many of his father's plans.[236]

Woods was not precluded from outside contracts, as he planned the gardens at Brizes,[237] Kelvedon Hatch in 1788, and landscaped for Harrison at Copford[238] (1784) and Stanway[239] in 1792 when he met Hutson (as described). The next year Woods died.

Brentwood provided two land surveyors before the end of the century. E. MARTIN is known only from an advertisement[240] (1788) of land for sale in which he styled himself "land surveyor". JOHN DEW, a bookseller and stationer, also called himself a land surveyor.[241] An undated map by him shows 25 acres in South Weald and in 1799 he surveyed 211 acres in Hanningfield for Filmer Honeywood. His map[243] looks old-fashioned with its divider over the scale bar and a flower at the centre of his compass rose. In 1800 Dew expanded his business to include appraisal and auctioneering. His son joined him, mapping[244] as J. Dew Jnr. (1809).

Five miles to the east of Brentwood lies Billericay, where HUGH JONES and ROBERT

Baroque cartouche from map by Thomas Browne (see p. 33) of the Waldegrave estates in Navestock, 1726 (see also illus. pp. 31 and 35).

MUNDEL lived. In 1773 Jones advertised[245] his services as a surveyor, adding that October was the best month for estate surveys. He invited "any young gentleman who is desirous of making himself a Master of the Art of Surveying" to take "the opportunity of being taught by real practice". He also sold sundials "suitable for any latitude" and "cheap but various sorts" for gardens. All this implies that his surveying career had started before 1773, but his first surviving survey was dated in the December of that year. His map[246] of 60 acres in Steeple is nicely decorated with a grey Adam type cartouche of a chain of flowers and knotted ribbon. The script is as clear as a typeface and the boundaries are shown as fence or hedge, with individual trees. His other known survey[247] was made in November 1774 of a small Buttsbury farm belonging to W. P. Johnson. The map is but a rough draft. However Jones may have surveyed more of Johnson's land as there is an undated anonymous copy of a map[248] of his farm in Fambridge.

Ten years later in Billericay Robert Mundel (1782) mapped[249] a 22 acre farm in Harlow for Mrs Newcomen of Billericay. He called it "an accurate map" but it is so badly executed that it must be the prime candidate for the ugliest estate map in the Essex Record Office. By a stroke of artistic justice it is Mundel's only surviving map. After making it Mundel announced[250] that he "now performed the business of appraiser and auctioneer". As such he sold household goods and stock from shops. But he continued to call himself a land surveyor right up to his last advertisement in 1798 when he had a farm to let. No doubt he was engaged in small land measurements for field alterations, which did not need a map. Lord Petre paid him ten shillings in 1796 for measuring tithe land in Buttsbury.

Throughout the century the metropolitan corner of south Essex seems to have had more than its fair share of "one-off" surveyors known only from one or two maps of that area. In this time period the glebe of Wanstead was surveyed[251] in May 1771 by JOHN HAY of "Leyton House" and the glebe of Little Ilford[252] was measured in 1775 by JOHN WICKSTEED. His map is a working draft on which his survey data are written; the glebe had been mapped in 1737 by Joseph Bland.

A rough plan, "the half size of the original map", showing Chingford Hall (243 a.) and the manor of Chingford St Pauls (700 a.), was made from a 1782 survey by WILLIAM BAKER and WILLIAM SNELL. The plan is in a memorandum book[253] of the manor, which was bought by the Snell family in 1709. A William Snell inherited the property in 1805; presumably he was the surveyor in 1782. Nothing else is known of this pair.

JAMES TURNBULL probably lived in Dagenham as he surveyed there in 1780 and 1790. His first map,[254] dated 1770, was of 89 acres in Little Warley on the unnecessarily large scale of 26.6 inches to a mile. The rococo cartouche is simple but well done. His "Sketch from a plan of Edolph's lands in Dagenham . . . drawn by James Turnbull, May 1780"[255] has an old-fashioned look and his 1790 Dagenham map[256] of a farm has a deliberately archaic look with the cartouche suggesting Elizabethan strap-work. However the buildings are shown in block plan, although the Checker Ale House is drawn in perspective and shows the inn sign.

JOHN HINDLEY[257] worked exclusively on the Barking and Dagenham estates of Bamber Gascoyne and so was most likely a resident in that area. In 1792 Hindley made a "true copy" of

Godson's 1732 survey of one of the farms on the estate and a year later surveyed "with a chain and cross-staff only" Bamber-Gascoyne's house and grounds in Barking. In 1794 Hindley assisted William Yates when he came down from Liverpool to survey all the Bamber-Gascoyne lands, not only in Essex but also the large holding in Lancashire.

Hindley's most remarkable contribution was his detailed commentary, written in 1804, on the 1799 copies of Yates' maps. His criticism of the Lancashire estate maps is confined to technicalities and it is obvious that he had no personal knowledge of the estate. However, his direct involvement with the Barking-Dagenham lands is equally obvious. He must have been a supervisor of these lands, as when writing the commentary he had "access to Mr Yates's large sheet map of these same farms – which may be depended upon, as it was (I believe) executed by his own hands". On another map he wrote "Mr Yates never surveyed any part of the Premises here mapped but Mr JH made him a copy whilst Mr Y was at Barking in the year 1794 of the old map . . . by James Bermingham in 1738." Hindley accompanied Yates throughout his survey, as indicated by a comment that "Mr Y walked over the farm measuring little or none", but carrying a copy of the old map made by Hindley.

The commentary is a mixture of sound technical criticism and lurid invective. Hindley must have been a peppery man. The copier of Yates' maps was dealt with severely. "I have at last got thro' this very tedious examination of Map 16 and its table, both most extraordinary productions, and whether the labour of two artists or one, fully entitling him or them to distinction and notoriety whose genius can not be confined, like that of a mere plodding copier, to the strict path of fidelity, truth and usefulness, but will continually break out, all manner of ways, into the Wilds of treachery, falsehood and confusion – the flighty regions of romance." Hindley was particularly critical of what was written on the maps and in the tables. The errors he considered "scandalous and shameless in the extreme. Surely the writing must have been done by an ignorant giddy lad, who neither knew the mischief of his blunders, nor cared about the matter."

His technical criticisms do highlight some important principles of cartography. A compass "should never be omitted in any map, or even a plan of a small piece of ground". A scale bar without details of the scale was useless, "the scale ought to be always defined as yards, chains & etc. – and if chains or poles of what dimension." In estatè maps "the situation of all the gates should be marked." He also alluded to the practice of copying maps using a pantograph, concluding that one of the maps he scrutinised "was done in the easiest and readiest mechanical manner, by means of a Pentagraph, which enlarges or diminishes copies; but unless it is an excellent instrument of the sort and most carefully managed considerable errors will occur from its use . . ."

J. VEVERS junior advertised[258] his services as a land surveyor in 1791 as an addition to his father's advertisement for his school, Whalebone House, near Romford. Land surveying was taught in the school, presumably by the son for in later years Vevers senior was advertising his school without a reference to his son, and with surveying omitted from the curriculum.

B. WADDINGTON made a "survey and plan of titheable lands in the manor of Waltham Holy Cross" in 1776. The map[259] is simple but large, covering 4000 acres without detail. It was made by order of Sir William Wake, who in 1767 had Parker of Thetford survey part of the Waltham Cross estate. There is no information on B. Waddington. A John Waddington and his son John were London surveyors up to 1773 and a Robert Waddington ran a London mathematical school up to 1778.

Scale bar by William Cole of Ramsden Belhus (see p. 54) from a map of Scots Hall, Canewdon 1720, with his characteristic style of decoration (cf. illus. p. 27).

References and Notes (Part II Third Period)

1 See his entries in the Catalogue of Maps in the ERO (1947).
2 Personal communication from Dr Hyde and his catalogue comments.
3 Maps in the Map Library, British Library.
4 Map in the Guildhall Library.
5 This account is taken from the Minute Book of Christ's Hospital, now in the Guildhall Library.
6 D/DP E47 (documents) and D/DP P55 (map).
7 These maps are in the Guildhall Library.
8 T/M 278.
9 D/DC 27/1119 and 1122.
10 D/DU 760 and D/DAr P11.
11 D/DQy 7.
12 D/DHt P27.
13 D/DCw P10, 11 & 25.
14 D/DCw P12. There is also a draft or copy of D/DCw P11 that has Doyley's name pencilled in as the surveyor.
15 Map in the Map Library, British Library.
16 T/M 134. Original map in Map Library, British Library.
17 The maps are in the Public Record Office.
18 D/DCw P18 & P2A &B.
19 In Southend branch of ERO.
20 D/DGe P15.
21 D/DQ 3/2.
22 Both maps in the Guildhall Library.
23 D/DTw P3.
24 T/M 232.
25 See G. Edwards; 1985. *London Topographical* Record XXV, 131. Mr Edwards also kindly supplied further details of Middleton's career.
26 H. M. Colvin; 1978. *A Biographical Dictionary of English Architects.*
27 D/DU 161/223.
28 D/DEl P27.
29 D/DXa 24.
30 D/DGe P22.
31 D/DU 682/1.
32 D/DW P5.
33 In *Chelmsford Chronicle.*
34 This appears to be true for London, but Samuel Harvey always described himself as an auctioneer and not as a land surveyor, despite his surveys.
35 D/DP P28.
36 D/DBz P2.
37 D/DCw P59.
38 D/DHt P21.
39 D/DS 140 & 127/3.
40 The maps are in Cambridge University Library.
41 See the Minute Book of Christ's Hospital, in the Guildhall Library.
42 Advertisement in *Chelmsford Chronicle.*
43 For an account of the Jupp family, carpenters and architects, see H. M. Colvin, Op. cit.
44 The maps are in the Guildhall Library.
45 The work of William and Charles Tomkins is outlined in –
   a. I. E. Benezit; 1966. *Dictionnaire des Peintres, Sculpteurs etc.*
   b. A. G. Graves (reprint 1970). *The Royal Academy of Arts. A complete Dictionary of Contributors.*
46 D/DSD 129.
47 D/DXa 22 (the marshes) & D/DGe P8 (Tillingham Hall).
48 D/P 339/3/5.
49 D/DDw P7.
50 D/DSN 16. The map notes T. F. Gepp as attorney for the Commissioners. An anonymous map (c. 1800) of Gepp's farm in Barling (D/DGe P24) is in Grist's style.
51 D/DU 304/53.
52 Trade card is in the Banks Collection, British Museum.
53 Facts kindly supplied by Miss G. L. Beech, assistant keeper of maps, Public Record Office.
54 Maps are in the Public Record Office (copies in ERO).
55 The maps (1797–99) are in Public Record Office (copies in ERO).
56 The map is in the Public Record Office and the 1762 plan in the Map Library, British Library.
57 The map is in the Public Record Office.
58 Map in the Map Library, British Library.

59 D/DGe P16.
60 An advertisement (1791) in the *Chelmsford Chronicle* for the sale of half a million trees at a Maidstone nursery directed enquiries to "Mr Hogben, land surveyors office, Boughton, near Canterbury".
61 D/Q 16 P6.
62 D/Q 18 P3.
63 D/DWe P7. Thomas Budgen may have been a descendant of Richard Budgen, who published a map of the county of Sussex in 1724.
64 From the *Dictionary of Land Surveyors*. Op. cit.
65 D/Sz 17.
66 T/M 512/3.
67 D/DU 435/3.
68 D/DSq 06 for details of diversion to "make the road more commodious to the public".
69 T/M 254.
70 "John Doyley, surveyor, assistant to James Asser" on a map of 1825.
71 Wills of Daniel (1798), David (1815) and Daniel (1819) Warner are in ERO and each man is named as a carpenter.
72 D/NC 2/13.
73 D/DGn 353–4.
74 D/DHt E4.
75 D/DP P153.
76 His maps are in the Hertfordshire Record Office.
77 D/DQy 10.
78 D/DW P8. Strictly speaking Moore was not an 18th century surveyor of Essex, as his only Essex map was dated 1800.
79 D/P 154/3/1.
80 D/DHw P12.
81 The maps and relevant documents are in the Public Record Office.
82 D/DEl P11.
83 D/DU 393/2.
84 D/DPa P3 & 4. See also D/DU 728/8, an undated anonymous map of Mrs Rawsthorne's land in Lexden. Was the surveyor Lewis?
85 Q/RDc 1.
86 From the *Dictionary of Land Surveyors*, Op. cit.
87 D/DB P31.
88 D/DU 584/1.
89 J. Blatchley & P. Eden; 1879. *Isaac Johnson of Woodbridge*. Suffolk Record Office.
90 D/DCm P2. Rush lived in Saxmundham, Suffolk. His father bought the Essex estates in the 1720s.
91 D/DB P4.
92 D/DQs 14.
93 D/DSm P7.
94 Both plans are in the Bedfordshire Record Office.
95 T/M 235.
96 D/DU 105/1.
97 Both maps are in the ERO.
98 D/DQy 74.
99 D/DQy 8.
100 T/M 166.
101 The maps are in the GLC Record Office.
102 Map in the GLC Record Office.
103 Several maps in Dorset Record Office. Mr H. Jacques, County Archivist, kindly helped with details.
104 T/M 457/3.
105 D/DAr P2.
106 See T. W. Hall, 1932. *The Fairbanks of Sheffield*.
107 D/DHt P22.
108 The book of maps is in the archives of the Marquis of Salisbury.
109 T/M 286.
110 D/DEl P16.
111 Advertisement in the *Chelmsford Chronicle*.
112 D/DQy 6.
113 See A. F. J. Brown; 1969. *Essex at Work*. ERO.
114 D/DEl P66.
115 D/DEl P82.
116 For a life of Cole see J. Bensusan-Butt; 1981. *East Anglian History Workshop Journal 2*, 3. Mr Bensusan-Butt also kindly provided further details on Cole and Dunthorne.
117 Advertisement in the *Ipswich Journal*.
118 D/DPb Z5. A comment by John Venn, vicar of Great Tey.

119 Taken from James Carter; 1845. *Memoirs of a Working Man.*
120 Advertisement in *Ipswich Journal.*
121 Maps and the note on Cole in the GLC Record Office.
122 D/DOt E3. Letters from Alston to his client Blair about Cole's survey of Little Horkesley and of the Rev. G. Whitmore's parish which was Lawford (next to Ardleigh).
123 C/T 623.
124 D/DDw P6.
125 Map in ERO (no index number).
126 D/DSu P1.
127 D/DU 381/36.
128 D/DR P14.
129 D/DOp P6.
130 D/DU 393/1.
131 D/DMb P20/1–3.
132 Advertisements in the *Chelmsford Chronicle.*
133 Item in the *Chelmsford Chronicle.*
134 D/P 263/8/2.
135 D/DBr P3.
136 In the *Chelmsford Chronicle.*
137 D/DGi F3/2.
138 D/DGi F8/19.
139 D/DU 591/62, 63, 64.
140 From the Land Tax Returns.
141 In the *Chelmsford Chronicle.*
142 D/DSL P3.
143 In the *Chelmsford Chronicle.*
144 D/DEs P3.
145 C/TS 54.
146 D/DU 509.
147 D/P 193/3/1.
148 D/DEl P10.
149 His maps are in the Suffolk and Hertfordshire Record Offices.
150 All the advertisements in the *Chelmsford Chronicle.*
151 D/DU 838/9–13, 15.
152 Advertisements over these years in the *Chelmsford Chronicle.*
153 D/DBm P3.
154 A letter (1778) written by a Governor of Guy's Hospital to Yeldham starts "I observe the plan you left me of New Mose Hall Farm." The simple anonymous plans of the farm are in the ERO but not in the same archive as the map of the whole estate. (Letter from the Hospital's Letter Book in the GLC Record Office.)
155 The map is in the Pasmore-Edwards Museum, Stratford.
156 D/DQ 86.
157 In the *Chelmsford Chronicle.*
158 Information kindly supplied by Mr Bensusan-Butt.
159 D/DFg P6 & 7.
160 The map is in the Guildhall Library.
161 T/M 313. The original map is in Wadham College, Oxford. This property is not on the College's estate maps of 1739–42.
162 T/M 562.
163 D/DDc P1.
164 In an advertisement in the *Chelmsford Chronicle.*
165 T/M 96–101.
166 T/M 102.
167 Miss M. Langstone kindly supplied these details.
168 D/DMy 15M50/91.
169 T/M 37.
170 In the *Chelmsford Chronicle.*
171 T/M 103.
172 D/DRa E16 fol. 94.
173 D/DRa 509.
174 The map is in the GLC Record Office.
175 D/DRa 016.
176 His signature as a collector is on the Terling Land Tax Returns.
177 In the *Chelmsford Chronicle.*
178 D/P 211/3 & D/DBo P2.
179 From an advertisement in the *Chelmsford Chronicle.*

180 The will is in the ERO.
181 In the *Chelmsford Chronicle*.
182 T/M 416.
183 D/DDc P2.
184 D/DU 19/26.
185 D/DDc P9/6 & 7.
186 D/DQ 50/2. The map title has "Lawling Hall".
187 D/DDw P5.
188 D/DMa P12.
189 D/DCf P.
190 D/DEl P15.
191 The accounts were written in a book (now in ERO, Southend) later used to record grave sites in Maldon. Also see F. W. Steer in *Essex Review 57*, 45.
192 Q/RUm 1/4.
193 Quotations from letters taken from the Letter Book of the Company now in ERO.
194 D/DS 121/1.
195 D/DMa P14.
196 D/DMa P14/2.
197 D/DU 649/7.
198 Original map in Wadham College, Oxford. T/M 309.
199 D/DPl 161.
200 Will in ERO.
201 Advertisement in *Chelmsford Chronicle*.
202 T/M 211. Moore's "banner" or "drape" for his titles is of the same design used by Bermingham. An anonymous undated map of land in Bobbingworth (T/M 210) has a different style of "drape", not by Moore.
203 D/DHt P52.
204 D/DHt P47.
205 D/DC 27/1115–7, 1120.
206 D/DC 27/1114.
207 D/DHt P20 & 57.
208 D/DFa P7/1–5.
209 D/DEs P2.
210 D/DFa P4.
211 D/DHt P42.
212 D/DHt P41.
213 D/DHt P23.
214 D/DHt P53.
215 D/DFa P5.
216 D/DFa P6.
217 D/DDa P1.
218 D/DBx P1.
219 A. S. Mason & J. Bensusan-Butt; 1988. *Proceedings of the Huguenot Society* XXIV: 508.
220 D/DHw E9.
221 D/DHw A2.
222 D/DFl E1.
223 The maps are in the Cambridge University Library.
224 Some of the estate maps by Rocque and by Scalé made for the Earl of Kildare are in the MS Department, British Library.
225 The map is in the Guildhall Library.
226 From advertisements in the *Chelmsford Chronicle*.
227 See the Land Tax Returns for Hutton.
228 In the *Chelmsford Chronicle*.
229 Hutson's surveys cover only two of the five properties shown on the earlier maps.
230 Advertisement in the *Chelmsford Chronicle*.
231 For a full account of Woods' work as a landscape gardener see Fiona Cowell; 1986–7. *Garden History 14*, 2 & *15*, 1 & 2.
232 D/DMd 39.
233 T/M 271.
234 D/DP P30.

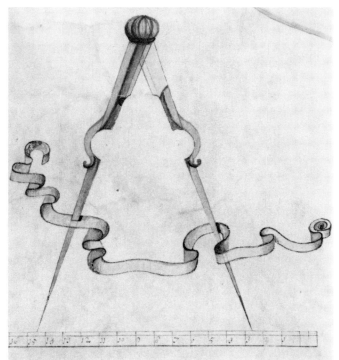

Divider and scale bar from a map of land in Thaxted by Thomas Holmes (see p. 47), 1702. Dividers and decorated scale bars, common throughout the 17th century, had fallen out of fashion by 1750 (see also illus. p. 59)

235 D/DP E68.
236 See Dorothy Stroud; 1975. *Capability Brown*. London.
237 D/DRo P1.
238 T/M 282.
239 Woods's plan was drawn on Middleton's map.
240 In the *Chelmsford Chronicle*.
241 Advertisement in the *Chelmsford Chronicle*. He was selling stationery to Lord Petre in 1796 (see Petre accounts in ERO).
242 D/DB P1.
243 D/Ke P2. Honeywood had Storer survey in Feering in 1796. The Honeywood lands in 1795 were surveyed anonymously.
244 D/DTw P9.
245 See *Chelmsford Chronicle*.
246 D/DCm P23.
247 D/DHt P16.
248 D/DHt P19.
249 D/DAr P8.
250 In the *Chelmsford Chronicle*.
251 D/P 292/3/3. A written survey in rector's cash book.
252 D/DP 175/3/2.
253 D/DU 158/1.
254 D/DQs 29.
255 The map is in Valence House Museum, Dagenham.
256 D/SH 24.
257 Hindley's maps and commentary are in the archives of the Marquis of Salisbury. Hindley, with his comments on scale, would have appreciated John Heather, who wrote on his 1721 map: "Measured by Mr Gunter's four pole chain divided into a hundred links each pole containing sixteen foot and a half and ploted on a scale of four chains in one inch".
258 In *Chelmsford Chronicle*.
259 D/DHt P58.

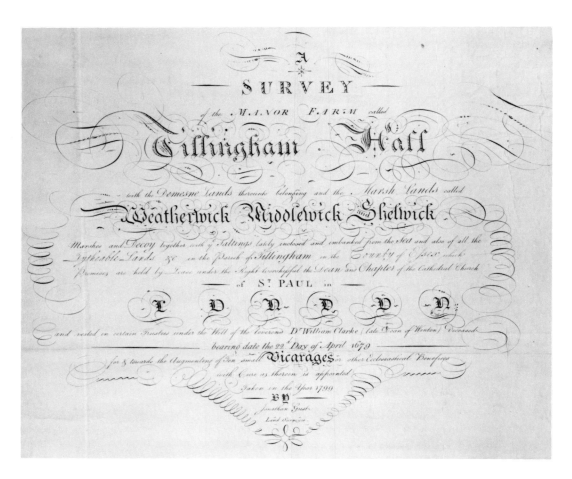

Title script by Jonathan Grist (see p. 105), 1799. The varied lettering styles and penned swashes point to the continuing influence of the writing-masters.

Index

This is a selective index of persons and places which appear in the text in a significant role.

In general, the inclusion of personal names has been limited to those of mapmakers, their patrons and those closely associated with the production of the maps.

Places have been indexed, wherever possible, at the parish level. For more localised place names (farms, manors, etc.) the reader should consult page references under the parish name.

The reference in bold type against a place name indicates the position of the parish on the map of Essex which appears on page 2 of the book.

Abdy, Sir Anthony *100*
Abdy, Sir Robert *37, 50*
Abdy, Thomas *37*
Abergavenny, Earl of *50*
Abington co. Cambs *49*
Acland Family *75*
Adams, John *9*
Affleck, Lady *115*
Agar, John *9*
Agnis, Benjamin *3, 6, 8, 47, 61n., 76, 79, 111*
Agnis, John *47, 111*
Aldham **2D,** *44*
Alefounder, Thomas Snr *vi, 12, 76, 97*
Alefounder, Thomas Jnr *76, 111*
Allen, John *8*
Allen, Thomas *9*
Alresford *40, 60n.*
Althorne **3D,** *47, 49*
André, Peter *ix, 25, 26*
Ansell, James *127*
Appleby, William Snr *50*
Archer, Lord *64, 91*
Archer, Thomas *36, 53, 91*
Ardleigh **2E,** *vi, 44, 46, 47, 109, 111, 115*
Argyll, Duke of *8*
Arkesden **1B,** *37, 73*
Armitage, Benjamin *110*
Arnold, Richard *91, 92*
Arther, Thomas *91 see also Archer, Thomas*
Ashdon **1B,** *39, 83, 86*
Asheldham **3D,** *44, 46, 56*
Ashford co. Kent *107*
Ashingdon **4D,** *26n.*
Ashurst, Robert *101, 107, 124, 131n.*
Asser, James *105*
Astle, Thomas *6, 64, 70, 71, 92, 93*
Aveley **4B,** *108*
Aylesbury co. Bucks *45*
Aylmer, Brabezon *51*
Aythorpe Roding **2B,** *69*

Bacons, Manor of, co. Suffolk *46*
Baddow *6, 56, 65, 81, 89, 124, 126*
Bainbridge, Thomas *98, 100, 101*
Baker, George *82, 85*
Baker, Robert *6, 9, 23, 88, 114, 115, 120, 132n.*
Baker, Robert Jnr *114, 120*
Baker, Samuel *107*
Baker, William *128*
Bamber, Dr *41, 68*
Bardfield **2C,** *85, 107*
Bardfield Saling **2C,** *83, 85, 127*
Barking **4A,** *36, 39, 68, 72, 106, 109, 128, 129*
Barling **4D,** *77, 100, 104, 115, 130n.*
Barnardiston, Sir Robert *38*
Barnes co. Surrey *100*
Barnston **2C,** *85*

Barrington Family *21, 34, 69, 108*
Barrow, J. *106*
Bate, Henry *9*
Bateman, Thomas *vi, 12, 58, 69*
Bayne, Charles *89*
Baynes, Bridge *74, 75*
Beauchamp Roding **3B,** *80, 103, 105*
Beaumont-cum-Moze **2F,** *26, 118*
Becket, Thomas *38, 39*
Bedford, Duke of *69*
Belchamp Otten **1C,** *78*
Belchamp St Paul **1C,** *96n.*
Belchamp Walter **1D,** *46, 78*
Bellamy, – *103, 126*
Bentfield, John *9*
Bentham, Jeremiah *79, 80*
Benyon, Richard *20, 35, 127*
Berden **1B,** *36, 37, 65, 98*
Bermingham, James *vi, 51, 67, 68, 72, 129, 133n.*
Beyton co. Suffolk *39*
Billericay **3B,** *6, 9, 79, 101, 127, 128*
Birch **2D,** *44, 45, 74, 77, 108, 114, 117*
Bird, Joseph *77*
Birdbrook **1C,** *vi, 51, 99*
Bishop's Stortford, co. Herts *6, 70, 108*
Black, William *20, 21, 28n.*
Blackmore **3B,** *123*
Blackmore, James *100*
Black Notley **2C,** *46, 78, 117*
Blair, Edward *24, 76*
Bland, Joseph *33, 71, 72, 128*
Blyth, John *77, 112, 113, 114, 115*
Boad, Henry *7, 9, 46*
Bobbingworth **3B,** *14, 37, 122, 133n.*
Bocking **2C,** *46, 74, 78, 85*
Bonnell Family *51*
Boothby, Robert *73*
Boreham **3C,** *3, 51, 80, 122*
Boughton co. Kent *131n.*
Bourginion, – *57, 63n., 89*
Bowles, John *9*
Bowra, John *72, 73*
Boxted **1E,** *111*
Bradbury, H. *9*
Bradfield **2E,** *64, 124*
Bradwell-juxta-Mare **3D,** *12, 51, 56, 65, 117*
Bragge, William *45*
Braintree **2C,** *9, 46, 49*
Bramston, George *52, 54*
Brantham, co. Suffolk *78*
Branton Hall, Manor, of, co. Suffolk *124*
Brasier, William *vi, 38, 40, 48, 55, 60n., 75, 90*
Braxted **2D,** *83, 117*
Braybrooke, Lord *20*
Brentwood **3B,** *6, 8, 9, 86, 88, 89, 91, 102, 120, 123, 127*
Bridgeman, Charles *57*
Brightlingsea **2E,** *101, 112, 114*

Bristol, Earl of *109*
Bristow, – *56*
Brock, J. *92*
Broomfield **3C,** *81, 115, 119, 121*
Brosgrove, – *126*
Brown, C. *9*
Browne, Thomas *vi, 17, 18, 19, 20, 24, 31, 33, 35, 39, 58n., 59n., 64, 104, 128*
Browse, Mrs *92*
Broxted **2B,** *14, 39, 54, 56, 110, 111*
Buchanan, John *9*
Buckingham, Duchess of *39*
Budgen, Thomas *107, 131n.*
Bulmer **1D,** *109*
Bulphan **4B,** *104*
Burges, John *40*
Burmash co. Kent *37*
Burnham *51, 113, 114, 125, 126*
Burrell, Sir Charles **4D,** *107*
Burrough Green co. Cambs *75*
Burstead **4B,** *32*
Bury St Edmunds, co. Suffolk *74, 109*
Butler, Joseph *4, 19, 24, 25, 99, 100*
Buttsbury **3C,** *6, 33, 54, 57, 63n., 79, 128*
Buxton, Dr *121*

Cadman, John *6, 92, 93*
Cambridge co. Cambs *75*
Canewdon **4D,** *vi, 56, 123, 126, 129*
Canfield **2B,** *39*
Canterbury co. Kent *38, 73, 106*
Canterbury Cathedral, Dean and Chapter of *38*
Canvey Island **4C,** *56, 106, 107, 126*
Cardigan, Earl of *40*
Carr, Backhouse *125, 126*
Carteret Family *64*
Case, John *119, 120*
Castle Hedingham **1C,** *47, 54*
Chamberlain, Thomas *72*
Chambers, George *110*
Chapman, John *25, 26, 28n., 113*
Chapman, Robert *75, 84*
Charterhouse, Governors of *39, 41, 57, 110, 113, 120*
Cheek, Edward *40*
Cheke, Richard *37*
Chelmer and Blackwater Navigation Company *20, 21, 121, 133n.*
Chelmsford **3C,** *6, 9, 24, 52, 79, 80, 85, 109, 122*
Chelmsford Grammar School, Governors of *51*
Chertsey co. Surrey *127*
Cheshunt Free School *73*
Chigwell **3A,** *vi, 33, 54, 68, 86, 88, 91, 123*
Childerditch **4B,** *56*
Childs Family *36, 53*

Childs, Richard *52*
Chingford **3A,** *73, 128*
Chipping Ongar **3A,** *122*
Chishall **1A,** *73, 74*
Chiswell, Richard *101, 111, 112*
Chrishall **1A,** *117*
Christ's Hospital, Governors of *4, 5, 7, 19, 24, 35, 36, 37, 41, 65, 70, 98, 99, 100, 104*
Clarke, John *38, 41*
Clarks, Robert *52*
Clavering **1B,** *65, 73, 98*
Clayton, Henry *127*
Cleer, Thomas *32, 33, 104*
Clergy, Corporation of Sons of *see Corporation of Sons of Clergy*
Clerk, J. *81, 85*
Cleveley, I. *92*
Cock, Benjamin *47*
Coffyn, John *4, 36, 37, 54, 56, 57, 63n., 77*
Coffyn, Mary *54, 56, 63n.*
Coggeshall **2D,** *9, 44, 47, 56, 81, 82, 84, 85*
Coggs, John *36*
Colchester **2E,** *4, 6, 7, 9, 32, 33, 43, 44, 45, 46, 47, 77, 82, 85, 104, 111, 112, 113, 114, 123, 124*
Coldham, Edward *74*
Cold Norton **3D,** *110, 120*
Cole, George *108*
Cole, William (of Colchester) *vi, 6, 8, 9, 14, 17, 19, 24, 77, 79, 108, 111, 112, 113, 114, 115, 119, 126, 131n., 132n.*
Cole, William (of Ramsden Belhus) *vi, 4, 24, 27, 36, 37, 52, 54, 56, 57, 63n., 79, 129*
Coley, Henry *45*
Collard, Richard *73*
Collier, Benjamin *36, 53*
Collins, Anthony *51*
Colmworth co. Beds *85*
Colne Engaine **2D,** *7*
Comberford, – *32*
Comyns, Richard *80*
Constable, Golding *21*
Conyers Family *8*
Conyers, Edward *41*
Conyers, John *65*
Cope, Robert *120*
Copford **2D,** *vi, 44, 46, 74, 77, 86, 112, 125, 126, 127*
Corfield, William *110*
Cornard co. Suffolk *46, 47*
Corporation of Sons of Clergy *39*
Cotton, Frances *104*
Cradock, James *4, 53, 62n.*
Crane, John *72, 73*
Creeksea **3D,** *49*
Creffield Family *4, 43, 44, 46, 48*
Creffield, George *4, 8, 46*
Cressing **2C,** *51*
Crippen, John *38*
Crow, James *17, 24, 33, 64*
Cunn, Samuel *7, 36*
Cushee, Richard *6, 36, 53*